# Essential Mathematics

## Book 7

# Answers

Elmwood Press

© David Rayner

First published 2001 by
Elmwood Press
80 Attimore Road
Welwyn Garden City
Herts. AL8 6LP

British Library Cataloguing in Publication Data

Rayner, David

   1. Mathematics—1961–
   1. Title

   ISBN 1 902 214 188

Typeset and illustrated by Tech-Set Ltd, Gateshead, Tyne and Wear
Printed in Great Britain by Cavalry Creative Services, 11 Bury Road,
Hatfield, Herts. AL10 8BJ

# BOOK 7    ANSWERS

## Part 1

*page 1*   ***Exercise 1***

**1.** (a) 1    (b) 24    (c) 30    (d) 17
**2.** 5                 **3.** 36                 **4.** 32                 **5.** $2\frac{1}{2}$                 **6.** 9
**7.** 45                 **8.** 19                 **9.** 30 000                 **10.** 2·5                 **11.** 81
**12.** −12                 **13.** −3                 **14.** 16                 **15.** 2                 **16.** 12·5
**17.** −4                 **18.** (a) 48    (b) 7    (c) 2    (d) 9                 **19.** 720                 **20.** $5 \times 7^2$
**21.** $\frac{5}{11}$                 **22.** 1440

*page 2*   ***Exercise 2***

**1.** 20, 25, 30, 35, 40
**2.** (a) 8, 10, 12, 14, 16          (b) 100, 96, 92, 88, 84          (c) 10, 20, 40, 80, 160          (d) 64, 32, 16, 8, 4
**3.** (a) 47                 (b) 3                 (c) 25, 51, 103, 207
**4.** (a) 28                 (b) 3                 (c) 1, 1, 1
**5.** (a) $+\frac{1}{2}$                 (b) ×2                 (c) add 0·1                 (d) divide by 3
**6.** (a) 8 squares in diagram     (b) circles: +8, +10, +12; boxes: 20, 30, 42
**7.** (a) 16 squares in shape     (b) circles: +7, +9, +11; boxes: 16, 25, 36
**8.** (a) 40 matches in square     (b) circles: +16, +20, +24; boxes: 40, 60, 84
**9.** (a) 0, 5, 10, 15, 20          (b) 1·3, 6·3, 11·3, 16·3, 21·3          (c) no
**10.** $5 \times 999 = 4995$, $6 \times 999 = 5994$, $7 \times 999 = 6993$
**11.** (a) $33\,333 \times 5 = 166\,665$, $333\,333 \times 5 = 1\,666\,665$     (b) $333\,333\,333 \times 5 = 1\,666\,666\,665$
**12.** (a) $5^2 + 5 + 6 = 36$, $6^2 + 6 + 7 = 49$, $7^2 + 7 + 8 = 64$     (b) $12^2 + 12 + 13 = 169$
**13.** (a) $654\,321 \times 9 = 5\,888\,889$     (b) $87\,654\,321 \times 9 = 788\,888\,889$
**14.** (a) $5 + 9 \times 1234 = 11\,111$     (b) $7 + 9 \times 123\,456 = 1\,111\,111$
**15.** (a) $6 \times 7 = 6 + 6 \times 6$     (b) $10 \times 11 = 10 + 10 \times 10$, $11 \times 12 = 11 + 11 \times 11$
**16.** $13 + 15 + 17 + 19 = 64 = 4^3$     $21 + 23 + 25 + 27 + 29 = 125 = 5^3$     $31 + 33 + 35 + 37 + 39 + 41 = 216 = 6^3$
**17.** (a) 1, 7, 21, 35, 35, 21, 7, 1     (b) 21, 28, 36     (c) sums are powers of 2

*page 6*   ***Exercise 1***

**1.** 9          **2.** 18          **3.** 7          **4.** 5          **5.** 42          **6.** 16          **7.** 105          **8.** 6          **9.** 52
**10.** 63          **11.** 18          **12.** 110          **13.** 720          **14.** 110          **15.** 109          **16.** 36          **17.** 99          **18.** 640
**19.** 6          **20.** 13

*page 7*   ***Exercise 2***

**1.** 13          **2.** 17          **3.** 1          **4.** 4          **5.** 40          **6.** 27          **7.** 2          **8.** 2          **9.** 80
**10.** 7          **11.** 27          **12.** 0          **13.** 3          **14.** 13          **15.** 78          **16.** 77          **17.** 28          **18.** 57
**19.** 3          **20.** 1          **21.** 1          **22.** 5          **23.** 3          **24.** 72          **25.** 5

*page 8*   ***Exercise 3***

**1.** 5          **2.** 9          **3.** 9          **4.** 36          **5.** 6          **6.** 9          **7.** 8          **8.** 56          **9.** 58
**10.** 18          **11.** 44          **12.** 99          **13.** 99          **14.** 8          **15.** 320          **16.** 420          **17.** 6          **18.** 70
**19.** 49          **20.** 81

*page 9* **Exercise 4**

| | | | | | | | | |
|---|---|---|---|---|---|---|---|---|
| **1.** 4 | **2.** 7 | **3.** 20 | **4.** 18 | **5.** 4 | **6.** 7 | **7.** 96 | **8.** 130 | **9.** 15 |
| **10.** 17 | **11.** 5 | **12.** 10 | **13.** 11 | **14.** 11 | **15.** 19 | **16.** 39 | **17.** 16 | **18.** 11 |
| **19.** 45 | **20.** 262 | **21.** 7 | **22.** 8 | **23.** 1 | **24.** 13 | **25.** 6 | **26.** 4 | **27.** 48 |
| **28.** 88 | **29.** 63 | **30.** 84 | **31.** 91 | **32.** 91 | | | | |

*page 10* **Exercise 5 Mystery machines**

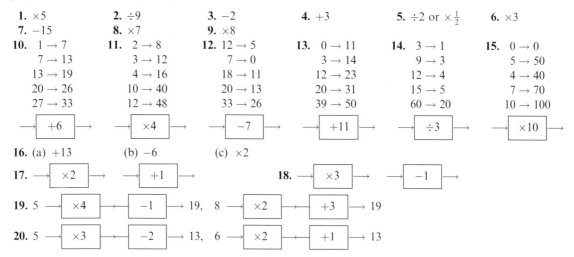

**1.** ×5    **2.** ÷9    **3.** −2    **4.** +3    **5.** ÷2 or ×$\frac{1}{2}$    **6.** ×3
**7.** −15    **8.** ×7    **9.** ×8

| **10.** $1 \to 7$ | **11.** $2 \to 8$ | **12.** $12 \to 5$ | **13.** $0 \to 11$ | **14.** $3 \to 1$ | **15.** $0 \to 0$ |
|---|---|---|---|---|---|
| $7 \to 13$ | $3 \to 12$ | $7 \to 0$ | $3 \to 14$ | $9 \to 3$ | $5 \to 50$ |
| $13 \to 19$ | $4 \to 16$ | $18 \to 11$ | $12 \to 23$ | $12 \to 4$ | $4 \to 40$ |
| $20 \to 26$ | $10 \to 40$ | $20 \to 13$ | $20 \to 31$ | $15 \to 5$ | $7 \to 70$ |
| $27 \to 33$ | $12 \to 48$ | $33 \to 26$ | $39 \to 50$ | $60 \to 20$ | $10 \to 100$ |
| → +6 → | → ×4 → | → −7 → | → +11 → | → ÷3 → | → ×10 → |

**16.** (a) +13    (b) −6    (c) ×2

**17.** → ×2 → → +1 →    **18.** → ×3 → → −1 →

**19.** 5 → ×4 → −1 → 19,    8 → ×2 → +3 → 19

**20.** 5 → ×3 → −2 → 13,    6 → ×2 → +1 → 13

*page 12* **Exercise 1**

| | | | |
|---|---|---|---|
| **1.** 30 | **2** 400 | **3.** 8 | **4.** 7 |
| **5.** 6000 | **6.** 30 000 | **7.** 5 000 000 | **8.** 700 000 |
| **9** 300 | **10.** 20 | **11.** 30 | **12.** 600 |
| **13.** 7000 | **14.** 40 | **15.** 400 | **16.** 70 000, 10 |

**17.** (a) 409    (b) 6401    (c) 16 211    (d) 500 000    (e) 450    (f) 3500
**18.** (a) 9652    (b) 2569
**19.** (a) six thousand two hundred    (b) ninety thousand
(c) twenty-five thousand and ten    (d) six hundred and ten thousand four hundred
(e) seven million ten thousand
**20.** (a) 98 643    (b) 34 698
**21.** (a) 361    (b) 409    (c) 7035
**22.** (a) 1425    (b) 7423    (c) 25 100
**23.** (a) | 4 | | 0 |    (b) 46 000
**24.** (a) 2058, 2136, 2142, 2290    (b) 5029, 5299, 5329, 5330    (c) 25 000, 25 117, 25 171, 25 200, 25 500
**25.** $n = 100$    **26.** $p = 10$    **27.** $a = 100, b = 7$    **28.** $p = 1000, q = 10$

*page 14* **Exercise 2**

| | | | |
|---|---|---|---|
| **1.** 545 | **2.** 2537 | **3.** 455 | **4.** 29 990 |
| **5.** 310 | **6.** 108 | **7.** 581 | **8.** 187 |
| **9.** 850 | **10.** 6000 | **11.** 365 | **12.** 1256 |
| **13.** 1648 | **14.** 7161 | **15.** 85 | **16.** 324 |

**17.** 1059      **18.** 325      **19.** $52\frac{1}{7}$      **20.** 92
**21.** 2313      **22.** 888      **23.** 7      **24.** 1080
**25.** 1492      **26.** 524      **27.** 840      **28.** 188
**29.** 1640      **30.** 385      **31.** 254      **32.** 18 800

*page 14*   **Exercise 3**

**1.** (a) 86 r 12   (b) $86\frac{2}{5}$    **2.** (a) 178 r 3   (b) $178\frac{3}{4}$    **3.** (a) 149 r 1   (b) $149\frac{1}{6}$
**4.** (a) 54 r 2   (b) $54\frac{2}{3}$    **5.** (a) 64 r 2   (b) $64\frac{1}{4}$    **6.** (a) 41 r 6   (b) $41\frac{2}{3}$
**7.** (a) 528 r 2   (b) $528\frac{2}{5}$    **8.** (a) 3570 r 1   (b) $3570\frac{1}{2}$    **9.** (a) 582 r 5   (b) $582\frac{5}{7}$
**10.** (a) 426 r 2   (b) $426\frac{2}{5}$    **11.** (a) 501 r 5   (b) $501\frac{5}{8}$    **12.** (a) 39 r 1   (b) $39\frac{1}{6}$
**13.** (a) 65 r 7   (b) $65\frac{7}{10}$    **14.** (a) 832 r 7   (b) $832\frac{7}{10}$    **15.** (a) 14 285 r 4   (b) $14\,285\frac{2}{3}$
**16.** (a) 536 r 2   (b) $536\frac{2}{9}$    **17.** (a) 286 r 5   (b) $286\frac{5}{7}$    **18.** (a) 1110 r 8   (b) $1110\frac{8}{9}$
**19.** (a) 612   (b) 612    **20.** (a) 12 080 r 3   (b) $12\,080\frac{3}{7}$

*page 15*   **Exercise 4**

**1.** 115      **2.** 1428 coins, 4 remaining      **3.** 5 teams of 4, rem. 3
**4.** 34      **5.** 13      **6.** 26
**7.** 9 tables      **8.** 12      **9.** 19
**10.** 7      **11.** 7      **12.** 55
**13.** (a) 2      (b) 6      (c) 5

*page 16*   **Exercise 5**   **Mixed problems**

**1.** 40      **2.** £384      **3.** 420      **4.** 847
**5.**

| × | 3 | 7 | 4 | 9 |
|---|---|---|---|---|
| 5 | 15 | 35 | 20 | 45 |
| 8 | 24 | 56 | 32 | 72 |
| 11 | 33 | 77 | 44 | 99 |
| 6 | 18 | 42 | 24 | 54 |

**6.** 1441      **7.** 1935      **8.** 120

**9.** 100, 250, 14 000      **10.** 18, 2000, 50 000      **11.** 1000, 50 000, 270 000
**12.** (a) $10 \times 10$   (b) $10 \times 10 \times 10$
**13.** (a) £5·50   (b) £55   (c) £5500   (d) £550 000      **14.** (a) £20   (b) £200   (c) £2000   (d) £2 000 000
**15.** There are many solutions. One solution is ...

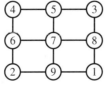

**16.** There are many solutions. One solution is ...

     **17.** $27 + 5 = 32$

**18.** 7200 min      **19.** add 31      **20.** add 101

*page 18* **Divisibility tests: an investigation**

**10.** if the number ends in zero

**A.**

| Number | Divisible by | | | | | | |
|---|---|---|---|---|---|---|---|
| | 2 | 3 | 4 | 5 | 6 | 8 | 9 |
| 363 | ✗ | ✓ | ✗ | ✗ | ✗ | ✗ | ✗ |
| 224 | ✓ | ✗ | ✓ | ✗ | ✗ | ✓ | ✗ |
| 459 | ✗ | ✓ | ✗ | ✗ | ✗ | ✗ | ✓ |
| 155 | ✗ | ✗ | ✗ | ✓ | ✗ | ✗ | ✗ |
| 168 | ✓ | ✓ | ✓ | ✗ | ✓ | ✓ | ✗ |
| 865 | ✗ | ✗ | ✗ | ✓ | ✗ | ✗ | ✗ |
| 360 | ✓ | ✓ | ✓ | ✓ | ✓ | ✓ | ✓ |
| 2601 | ✗ | ✓ | ✗ | ✗ | ✗ | ✗ | ✓ |

**B.** 37 177 Yes, 8498 Yes, 431 781 Yes, 42 329 Yes, 39 579 No, 910 987 Yes

*page 19* **Exercise 6**

**1.** (a) $\begin{array}{r} 314 \\ +463 \\ \hline 777 \end{array}$ (b) $\begin{array}{r} 354 \\ +624 \\ \hline 978 \end{array}$ (c) $\begin{array}{r} 358 \\ +144 \\ \hline 502 \end{array}$ **2.** (a) $\begin{array}{r} 536 \\ +214 \\ \hline 750 \end{array}$ (b) $\begin{array}{r} 246 \\ +357 \\ \hline 603 \end{array}$ (c) $\begin{array}{r} 634 \\ +284 \\ \hline 918 \end{array}$

**3.** (a) $\begin{array}{r} 37 \\ \times\ 5 \\ \hline 185 \end{array}$ (b) $\begin{array}{r} 47 \\ \times\ 9 \\ \hline 423 \end{array}$ (c) $\begin{array}{r} 374 \\ \times\ 8 \\ \hline 2992 \end{array}$

**4.** (a) $231 \div 7 = 33$ (b) $13 \times 11 = 143$ (c) $12 \times 9 = 108$ (d) $918 \div 6 = 153$

**5.** (a) $\begin{array}{r} 856 \\ -324 \\ \hline 532 \end{array}$ (b) $\begin{array}{r} 832 \\ -415 \\ \hline 417 \end{array}$ (c) $\begin{array}{r} 645 \\ -288 \\ \hline 357 \end{array}$

**6.** (a) $55 \times 8 = 440$ (b) $21 \times 11 = 231$ (c) $400 \div 8 = 50$ (d) $978 \div 6 = 163$
**7.** (a) $79 + 48 = 127$ (b) $512 - 49 = 463$ (c) $653 - 487 = 166$ (d) $875 - 579 = 296$
**8.** (a) (b) (c) (d) various answers **9.** (a) $4 \times 4 - 4 = 12$ (b) $8 \div 8 + 8 = 9$ (c) $8 \times 8 + 8 = 72$
**10.** (a) $+$ (b) $\div$ (c) $\times$ (d) $\div$ (e) $-$ **11.** (a) $+$ (b) $-, -$ (c) $+$

*page 22* **Exercise 1**

**1.** A, cube — B, cuboid — C, triangular prism — D, hexagonal based prism — H, cylinder
**2.** E, triangular based pyramid or tetrahedron — F, square based pyramid — G, cone — I, sphere and J, hemisphere
**3.** various possible answers

*page 23* **Exercise 2**

**1.** B  6 faces, 12 edges, 8 vertices
  C  5 faces, 9 edges, 6 vertices
**2.** cuboids  6 faces, 12 edges, 8 vertices

**3.** triangular prisms   5 faces, 9 edges, 6 vertices
**4.** remaining shape:   7 faces, 15 edges, 10 vertices
   piece cut off:   4 faces, 6 edges, 4 vertices
**5.** various answers      **6.** various answers
**7.**

**8.** $F + V - 2 = E$

|   | faces | edges | vertices |
|---|---|---|---|
| A | 6 | 12 | 8 |
| B | 6 | 12 | 8 |
| C | 5 | 9 | 6 |
| D | 8 | 18 | 12 |
| E | 4 | 6 | 4 |
| F | 5 | 8 | 5 |

*page 25*   **Exercise 3**

**1.** (c) does not make a cube, (a), (b), (d), (e) do make cubes
**2.** (a) C        (b) F        (d) D        (e) C

*page 28*   **Exercise 1**

**1.** T            **2.** T            **3.** T            **4.** T            **5.** T            **6.** F            **7.** F            **8.** F
**9.** T            **10.** F           **11.** T           **12.** T           **13.** T           **14.** T           **15.** T           **16.** T
**18.** 7 is $\frac{7}{100}$ths, 2 is $\frac{2}{10}$ths, 1 is $\frac{1}{1000}$th        **19.** 3 is $\frac{3}{10}$ths, 6 is $\frac{6}{1000}$ths, 8 is $\frac{8}{100}$ths
**20.** (a) 0·3            (b) 0·07            (c) 0·11            (d) 0·004            (e) 0·16            (f) 0·016
**21.** (a) +0·4           (b) +0·005          (c) −0·2            (d) −0·06

*page 29*   **Exercise 2**

**1.** 0·12, 0·21, 0·31            **2.** 0·04, 0·35, 0·4            **3.** 0·67, 0·672, 0·7
**4.** 0·045, 0·05, 0·07          **5.** 0·089, 0·09, 0·1          **6.** 0·57, 0·705, 0·75
**7.** 0·041, 0·14, 0·41          **8.** 0·8, 0·809, 0·81          **9.** 0·006, 0·059, 0·6
**10.** 0·143, 0·15, 0·2          **11.** 0·04, 0·14, 0·2, 0·53    **12.** 0·12, 0·21, 1·12, 1·2
**13.** 0·08, 0·75, 2·03, 2·3     **14.** 0·26, 0·3, 0·602, 0·62   **15.** 0·5, 1·003, 1·03, 1·3
**16.** 0·709, 0·79, 0·792, 0·97  **17.** 0·312, 0·321, 1·04, 1·23 **18.** 0·008, 0·075, 0·09, 0·091
**19.** 2, 2·046, 2·05, 2·5       **20.** 1·95, 5·1, 5·19, 9·51    **21.** My teacher is ...
**22.** (a) 3·37    (b) 14·9    (c) 0·941      **23.** (a) 11·26    (b) 1·304    (c) 0·392
**24.** (a) 3·143    (b) 2·719    (c) 1·415
**25.** (a) £0·11    (b) £0·02    (c) £0·05    (d) £0·10    (e) £0·20    (f) £0·50

*page 30*   **Exercise 3**

**1.** 46            **2.** 2·6            **3.** 14·8            **4.** 15·2            **5.** 0·2            **6.** 3·2
**7.** 7             **8.** 5·2            **9.** 3·14            **10.** 0·02           **11.** 1·02           **12.** 0·8
**13.** 0·24         **14.** 120           **15.** 1·8            **16.** 16            **17.** 88            **18.** 4·35
**19.** 2·75         **20.** 3·55          **21.** 0·16           **22.** 72·5          **23.** 18·3          **24.** 3·13

*page 31*   **Exercise 4**

16·61
**1.** 5·26            **2.** 7·27            **3.** 16·16            **4.** 2·128            **5.** 13·045            **6.** 40·554
**7.** 21·67           **8.** 12·45           **9.** 465·601          **10.** 44·321           **11.** 13·852           **12.** 19·77

**13.** 15·6     **14.** 24·4     **15.** 51·9     **16.** 5·3     **17.** 2·41     **18.** 19·78
**19.** 88·73     **20.** 1·556     **21.** 24·084     **22.** 1·728     **23.** 0·986     **24.** 8·26
**25.** (a) $8·56 - 4·83 = 3·73$    (b) $4·07 + 4·96 = 9·03$    (c) $3·176 - 2·428 = 0·748$
**26.** £1     **27.** £1, 50p, 20p, 5p, 2p, 1p     **28.** £36·10

*page 32*   **Exercise 1**

**1.** (a) 70    (b) 60    (c) 20    (d) 100    (e) 60    (f) 130
   (g) 240    (h) 20    (i) 30    (j) 590    (k) 40    (l) 50
**2.** (a) 600    (b) 300    (c) 600    (d) 900    (e) 300    (f) 700
   (g) 200    (h) 1500
**3.** (a) 5000    (b) 1000    (c) 1000    (d) 2000    (e) 1000    (f) 3000
   (g) 26 000    (h) 14 000
**4.** (a) 14    (b) 81    (c) 216    (d) 59    (e) 40    (f) 23
   (g) 122    (h) 12    (i) 23    (j) 156    (k) 6    (l) 21

*page 34*   **Exercise 2**

**1.** (a) 2·4   (b) 8·9   (c) 4·7   (d) 12·5      **2.** (a) 1·92   (b) 4·07   (c) 10·00   (d) 65·37
**3.** (a) 18·8   (b) 3·6   (c) 17·1   (d) 0·8   (e) 5·4   (f) 11·3   (g) 10·3   (h) 7·1
**4.** (a) 3·76   (b) 11·64   (c) 0·38   (d) 138·30   (e) 11·44   (f) 7·06   (g) 6·58   (h) 5·31
**5.** (a) 8·417   (b) 0·74   (c) 18·215   (d) 18·1   (e) 0·075   (f) 0·03   (g) 1·36   (h) 10·0   (i) 0·456
**6.** (a) 1·57   (b) 19·36   (c) 0·23   (d) 2·23   (e) 1·24   (f) 4·56   (g) 74·62   (h) 7·89
**7.** (a) 8·3 cm   (b) 2·2 cm   (c) 10·9 cm   (d) 5·5 cm   (e) 12·8 cm
**8.** (i) length 5·2 cm, width 3·6 cm, Area $= 18·7\,\text{cm}^2$
   (ii) length 6·8 cm, width 2·7 cm, Area $= 18·4\,\text{cm}^2$

*page 35*   **Exercise 3**

**1.** C     **2.** B     **3.** B     **4.** A     **5.** B
**6.** C     **7.** A     **8.** C     **9.** B     **10.** C
**11.** C     **12.** C     **13.** A     **14.** B     **15.** B
**16.** A     **17.** C     **18.** C     **19.** C     **20.** B
**21.** £140/£150     **22.** £4800     **23.** £300
**24.** (a) 48·99    (b) 1·96    (c) 214·2    (d) 15·33    (e) 103·8    (f) 7·657
**25.** (a) 20·64    (b) 52·56    (c) 200·9    (d) 1·19    (e) 9·13    (f) 0·14

*page 37*   **Exercise 1**

**1.** 8     **2.** 25     **3.** 35     **4.** 22     **5.** 54     **6.** 29
**7.** 60     **8.** 45     **9.** 93     **10.** 101     **11.** 76     **12.** 29

*page 38*   **Exercise 2**

**1.** 3     **2.** 6     **3.** 4     **4.** $7\frac{1}{2}$     **5.** 3     **6.** $4\frac{1}{2}$
**7.** 3     **8.** 3     **9.** $40\,\text{cm}^2$     **10.** $45\frac{1}{2}\,\text{cm}^2$     **11.** $59\frac{1}{2}\,\text{cm}^2$     **12.** $95\,\text{cm}^2$
**13.** $30\,\text{cm}^2$     **14.** $34\,\text{cm}^2$     **15.** $90\,\text{cm}^2$     **16.** 2·4 cm     **17.** 2·25 cm     **18.** 12 cm
**19.** 5 cm     **20.** 4 cm     **21.** 8 cm     **22.** 7 cm     **23.** 8 cm

*page 40* **Exercise 3**

(All in square units).

1. $10\frac{1}{2}$  2. 9  3. 8  4. $12\frac{1}{2}$  5. $10\frac{1}{2}$  6. 14
7. 14  8. 10  9. 12  10. $18\frac{1}{2}$  11. 23  12. $29\frac{1}{2}$
13. 47  14. $\frac{3}{4}$ cm$^2$  15. $\frac{1}{3}$

*page 41* **Exercise 4**

1. (a) 14 cm  (b) 12 cm  (c) 12 cm  2. (a) 12 cm  (b) 14 cm  (c) 12 cm
3. (a) 23 cm  (b) 24 cm  (c) 21 cm  (d) 12 cm  (e) 80 cm  (f) 30 cm
4. 22 cm  5. 26 cm  6. 22 cm  7. 24 cm  8. 28 cm  9. 34 cm
10. 26 cm  11. 32 cm  12. (a) B  (b) A and D  14. 44 cm
15. (a) E  (b) C  (c) B  16. 13 m  17. length = 12 cm  width = 8 cm  height = 3 cm

*page 44* **Exercise 5**

1. 192 cm$^2$  2. 80  3. 16  4. (a) 24 cm$^2$  (b) 20 cm$^2$
5. 50 hectares  6. 200 m  7. £30 000  9. 84 cm$^2$
10. 48·75 m$^2$  11. £3250  12. 50  13. 1100 m
14. (a) 63 m$^2$  (b) £31·20  15. 195 m$^2$, £3·90

# Part 2

*page 46* **Exercise 1**

1. $\frac{1}{3}$  2. $\frac{2}{9}$  3. $\frac{1}{3}$  4. $\frac{1}{4}$  5. $\frac{2}{5}$  6. $\frac{1}{3}$  7. $\frac{1}{4}$  8. $\frac{1}{4}$  9. $\frac{1}{2}$
10. 1  11. 3  12. 2  13. 1  14. 4  15. 2  16. 3  17. 3  19. 6
20. 6  21. 2  22. 9  23. 3  24. 35  25. 3  26. (b)  27. (b)  28. $\frac{4}{9}$
29. $\frac{3}{10}$  30. $\frac{3}{4}$  31. $\frac{9}{15}$  32. $\frac{5}{8}$  33. $\frac{5}{12}$

*page 48* **Exercise 2**

1. $3\frac{1}{2}$  2. $1\frac{2}{3}$  3. $2\frac{1}{3}$  4. $1\frac{1}{4}$  5. $2\frac{2}{3}$  6. $1\frac{1}{3}$
7. 3  8. $4\frac{1}{2}$  9. $2\frac{1}{4}$  10. 5  11. $1\frac{2}{3}$  12. $1\frac{3}{7}$
13. $1\frac{5}{8}$  14. $2\frac{1}{3}$  15. 2  16. 12  17. $3\frac{1}{7}$  18. $1\frac{2}{3}$
19. $2\frac{2}{5}$  20. $1\frac{1}{2}$  21. $\frac{5}{4}$  22. $\frac{4}{3}$  23. $\frac{9}{4}$  24. $\frac{8}{3}$
25. $\frac{15}{8}$  26. $\frac{5}{3}$  27. $\frac{22}{7}$  28. $\frac{13}{6}$  29. $\frac{19}{4}$  30. $\frac{15}{2}$
31. $\frac{29}{8}$  32. $\frac{22}{5}$  33. $\frac{17}{5}$  34. $\frac{33}{4}$  35. $\frac{13}{10}$

*page 48* **Exercise 3**

1. 40  2. 30  3. 10  4. 20
5. 156  6. 69  7. £310  8. £1000
9. 64 kg  10. 36  11. 8  12. 21
13. 88 cm  14. $\frac{27}{100}, \frac{97}{100}, \frac{1}{4}, \frac{1}{1000}, \frac{1}{365}, \frac{31}{365}$  15. (a) 12  (b) 8  16. 22·5 litres
17. 2·80 m, 1·96 m  19. $\frac{1}{2} + \frac{1}{4} + \frac{1}{6} + \frac{1}{12}$  20. $\frac{1}{2} + \frac{1}{3} + \frac{1}{6}$

*page 50*  **Exercise 4**

**1.** $\frac{3}{5}$    **2.** $\frac{3}{7}$    **3.** $\frac{5}{6}$    **4.** $\frac{4}{8}$    **5.** $\frac{5}{9}$    **6.** $\frac{7}{10}$    **7.** $\frac{5}{11}$    **8.** $\frac{3}{25}$

**9.** $\frac{1}{2} = \frac{2}{4}, \frac{3}{4}$    **10.** $\frac{1}{4} = \frac{2}{8}, \frac{3}{8}$    **11.** $\frac{1}{2} = \frac{4}{8}, \frac{7}{8}$    **12.** $\frac{1}{2} = \frac{8}{16}, \frac{9}{16}$

**13.** $\frac{1}{2} = \frac{2}{4}, \frac{1}{4}$    **14.** $\frac{1}{4} = \frac{2}{8}, \frac{3}{8}$    **15.** $\frac{1}{4} = \frac{2}{8}, \frac{1}{8}$    **16.** $\frac{1}{2} = \frac{4}{8}, \frac{1}{8}$

**17.** $\frac{2}{3} = \frac{4}{6}, \frac{5}{6}$    **18.** $\frac{4}{5} = \frac{8}{10}, \frac{9}{10}$    **19.** $\frac{2}{5} = \frac{4}{10}, \frac{7}{10}$    **20.** $\frac{1}{3} = \frac{2}{6}, \frac{3}{6}$

**21.** $\frac{1}{2} = \frac{4}{8}, \frac{3}{8}$    **22.** $\frac{2}{3} = \frac{4}{6}, \frac{3}{6}$    **23.** $\frac{1}{10} = \frac{2}{20}, \frac{1}{20}$    **24.** $\frac{3}{4} = \frac{6}{8}, \frac{3}{8}$

**26.** Many answers, e.g. $\frac{1}{2} + \frac{4}{8}, \frac{1}{5} + \frac{8}{10}$ etc

*page 51*  **Exercise 1**

**1.** C(4, 4), D(1, 2), E(7, 3), F(3, 0), G(2, 1), H(0, 3), I(6, 5)
**2.** (a) (4, 8)    (b) (7, 4)    (c) (6, 7)    (d) (3, 4)    (e) (8, 4)    (f) (5, 2)
**3.** (a) Hand grenade area          (b) Parachute drop zone          (c) Secret caves
   (d) Hospital C                   (e) Interrogation centre          (f) Helicopter pad
   (g) Hospital B                   (h) Look-out point

*page 52*  **Exercise 2**

**1.** What do you call a man with a spade in his head? Doug
**2.** What do you call a man without a spade in his head? Douglas
**3.** What do you call a dead parrot? Polygon
**4.** With what do you stuff a dead parrot? Polyfilla.

*page 55*  **Exercise 4**

**1.** (a) (7, 7), (4, 6)    (b) (5, 11), (3, 10)    (c) (7, 3) (4, 2)    (d) (9, 0), (9, 2)    (e) (11, 7), $(10\frac{1}{2}, 9\frac{1}{2})$
**2.** P: (3, 6), (7, 2), (1, 2)    Q: (12, 4), (8, 6), (12, 12)
**3.** (4, 3), (1, 5), (3, 1), (2, 7), (5, 6), (0, 2), (0, 4), (1, 4), (1, 6), (4, 2), (4, 4), (5, 4)
**4.** (a) (7, 3), (1, 5), (5, 1), (3, 7), (5, 3), (3, 5), (8, 0), (0, 8) etc
   (b) Any points on the line $x + y = 8$
**5.** (a) (−4, −1)    (b) (1, 3)    (c) (1, 0)    **6.** (a) (−1, −3)    (b) (3, 3)    (c) (−2, 5)
**7.** kite: (−3, 1), (−3, 2) … (many others)
   trapezium: (5, 2), (2, 0), …
   trapezium: (5, −2), (5, −1), …

*page 58*  **Exercise 1**

| | | | | |
|---|---|---|---|---|
| **1.** 2M | **2.** $N + 6$ | **3.** $e − 3$ | **4.** $d + 10$ | **5.** 3N |
| **6.** $2x + 3$ | **7.** $2y − 7$ | **8.** $3k + 10$ | **9.** $100s$ | **10.** $6t + 11$ |
| **11.** $p = 3a$ | **12.** $4b$ | **13.** $5c$ | **14.** $6d$ | **15.** $2e + 2f$ |
| **16.** $2g + h$ | **17.** $2l + 8$ | | | |

*page 59*  **Exercise 2**

| | | | | |
|---|---|---|---|---|
| **1.** $x + y − 3$ | **2.** $2N + T$ | **3.** $p + t − x$ | **4.** $3b + c$ | **5.** $\frac{M}{2} + 7$ |
| **6.** $3x − z + 3$ | **7.** $10N + M$ | **8.** $3p − 2x$ | **9.** $l − 4\,\text{cm}$ | **10.** $25 − x\,\text{m}$ |
| **11.** $h + t − 30\,\text{cm}$ | **12.** $6w$ | **13.** $\frac{N}{4}$ | **14.** $3n + 50$ | **15.** $\frac{x}{5}$ |

*page 61*   **Exercise 3**

| | | | | |
|---|---|---|---|---|
| **1.** $5x$ | **2.** $9a$ | **3.** $3a + 2b$ | **4.** $7y$ | **5.** $9x$ |
| **6.** $3d$ | **7.** $4x + 3$ | **8.** $10d$ | **9.** $12y$ | **10.** $6d - 4$ |
| **11.** $6x + 3y$ | **12.** $6h$ | **13.** $2y$ | **14.** $4x$ | **15.** $8a$ |
| **16.** $3a + b$ | **17.** $4 - 2x$ | **18.** $4d$ | **19.** $6a$ | **20.** $15t$ |
| **21.** $22b$ | **22.** $14c$ | **23.** $4c$ | **24.** $5c - 5$ | **25.** $10a$ |
| **26.** $9a + 9$ | **27.** $11b - 11$ | **28.** $10b$ | | |

*page 62*   **Exercise 4**

| | | | | |
|---|---|---|---|---|
| **1.** $9x + 8y$ | **2.** $12x + 3y$ | **3.** $3a + 2y$ | **4.** $10t + 3$ | **5.** $9y + 10$ |
| **6.** $x + 9b$ | **7.** $4a + 8$ | **8.** $9h + 7y$ | **9.** $9y + 6$ | **10.** $3x + 13$ |
| **11.** $4x + 10y$ | **12.** $14y + 1$ | **13.** $a + 3c$ | **14.** $10x + 9y$ | **15.** $d + 6$ |
| **16.** $3a + 2c - 5d$ | **17.** $7x + 7$ | **18.** $7x - 2y + 4$ | **19.** $13y + 1$ | **20.** $3a + 6c$ |
| **21.** $d + 4$ | **22.** $10a - 9$ | **23.** $12a + 5c$ | **24.** $y + 9$ | **25.** $12y + 3x$ |
| **26.** $10c + 6d$ | **27.** $10a + 4y$ | **28.** $a + 2c$ | **29.** $5x + 9y + 9$ | **30.** $14a + 3x$ |

*page 62*   **Exercise 5**

| | | | | | |
|---|---|---|---|---|---|
| **1.** T | **2.** F | **3.** T | **4.** T | **5.** T | **6.** T |
| **7.** F | **8.** T | **9.** F | **10.** F | **11.** F | **12.** T |

**13.** (a) $m = 100 - n$   (b) $a = 15 \div b$   (c) $c = 20 + d$

**14.** (a) $5a$   (b) $3n - 2$   (c) $m + 2n + p$   (d) $1$   (e) $n$   (f) $a$

**15.** $13 + 7, 9 + 11$   (b) $20 \times 5, 25 \times 4$   (c) $1^2 \times 8, 4^2 \times \frac{1}{2}$

**16.** (a) $11$   (b) $11$   (c) $20$   (d) $28$   (e) $36$   (f) $18$

*page 63*   **Number walls: an investigation**

Part A: Largest total obtained by putting largest numbers in the middle of the base, smallest numbers at either end.

Part D: Pupils should be encouraged (and helped) to use algebra.

With 3 bricks: Top brick $= a + 2b + c$

With 4 bricks: Top brick $= a + 3b + 3c + d$

With 5 bricks: Top brick $= a + 4b + 6c + 4d + e$

Pascal's triangle can be seen in the coefficients.

*page 64*   **Exercise 6**

| | | | |
|---|---|---|---|
| **1.** $\square = 8$ | **2.** $\bigcirc = 5$ | **3.** $\bigcirc = 12$ | **4.** $\square = 4$ |
| **5.** $\triangle = 3$ | **6.** $\triangle = 4$ | **7.** $\square = 12$ | **8.** $\triangle = 10$ |
| **9.** $\triangle = 14$ | **10.** $\square = 8$ | **11.** $\bigcirc = 9$ | **12.** $\bigcirc = 5$ |

*page 65*   **Exercise 7**

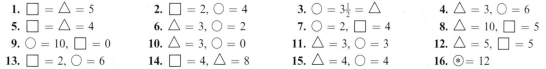

| | | | |
|---|---|---|---|
| **1.** $\square = \triangle = 5$ | **2.** $\square = 2, \bigcirc = 4$ | **3.** $\bigcirc = 3\frac{1}{2} = \triangle$ | **4.** $\triangle = 3, \bigcirc = 6$ |
| **5.** $\square = \triangle = 4$ | **6.** $\triangle = 3, \bigcirc = 2$ | **7.** $\bigcirc = 2, \square = 4$ | **8.** $\triangle = 10, \square = 5$ |
| **9.** $\bigcirc = 10, \square = 0$ | **10.** $\triangle = 3, \bigcirc = 0$ | **11.** $\triangle = 3, \bigcirc = 3$ | **12.** $\triangle = 5, \square = 5$ |
| **13.** $\square = 2, \bigcirc = 6$ | **14.** $\square = 4, \triangle = 8$ | **15.** $\triangle = 4, \bigcirc = 4$ | **16.** $\circledast = 12$ |

*page 67*  **Exercise 1**

**2.** (a) 15%  (b) 5%  (c) 45%  (d) 60%  (e) 75%

**3.** (a) A $= \frac{1}{2}$, B $= \frac{4}{5}$, C $= \frac{1}{4}$, D $= \frac{1}{5}$, E $= \frac{3}{10}$, F $= \frac{1}{4}$, G $= \frac{1}{3}$, H $= \frac{2}{5}$

(b) A = 50%, B = 80%, C = 25%, D = 20%, E = 30%, F = 25%, G $= 33\frac{1}{3}$%, H = 40%

**4.** (a) $\frac{3}{10}$  (b) 75%  (c) $33\frac{1}{3}$%  (d) $\frac{1}{100}$  (e) $\frac{4}{5}$  (f) 10%

**5.** (a) 25%  (b) 75%  (c) 60%  (d) 20%  (e) 50%

**6.** (a) 75%  (b) 60%  (c) 75%  (d) $33\frac{1}{3}$%  (e) 50%  (f) 25%

*page 69*  **Exercise 2**

**1.** (a) £10  (b) £9  (c) £9  (d) £1000  (e) £30  (f) £12
**2.** (a) £90  (b) $12  (c) £8  (d) $600  (e) £3  (f) £5
**3.** £3  **4.** 36  **5.** 180
**6.** (a) £45  (b) £7·50  (c) £16  (d) £36  (e) £20  (f) £15
**7.** (a) £1050  (b) £77  (c) £15·05  **8.** £7755  **9.** £37 800  **10.** £9

*page 70*  **Exercise 3**

**1.** (a) £170·50  (b) £10·56  (c) £212·80  (d) £24·36  (e) £0·63  (f) £480
**2.** (a) 5·04 km  (b) 3880 kg  (c) 140 m  (d) $21 700  (e) 79·52 km  (f) $11·16
**3.** (a) £0·93  (b) £3·57  (c) £0·48  (d) £2·94  (e) £0·39  (f) £243·96
**4.** (a) £23  (b) £220  (c) £4000  (d) £40  (e) £100  (f) £9
**5.** 0·51 kg  **6.** 32  **7.** 1·92 g  **8.** £2·85  **9.** (a) 91  (b) 49
**10.** (a) 441  (b) 392  **11.** £29 900

*page 72*  **Practice questions**

| | | | | | | |
|---|---|---|---|---|---|---|
| **A** | **1.** 37 | **2.** 47 | **3.** 46 | **4.** 81 | **5.** 107 | **6.** 97 |
| | **7.** 57 | **8.** 77 | **9.** 43 | **10.** 258 | **11.** 137 | **12.** 315 |
| **B** | **1.** 81 | **2.** 93 | **3.** 101 | **4.** 81 | **5.** 57 | **6.** 55 |
| | **7.** 101 | **8.** 47 | **9.** 103 | **10.** 92 | **11.** 18 | **12.** 311 |
| **C** | **1.** 88 | **2.** 88 | **3.** 75 | **4.** 105 | **5.** 74 | **6.** 49 |
| | **7.** 39 | **8.** 102 | **9.** 129 | **10.** 54 | **11.** 94 | **12.** 25 |
| **D** | **1.** 108 | **2.** 76 | **3.** 134 | **4.** 146 | **5.** 56 | **6.** 158 |
| | **7.** 230 | **8.** 252 | **9.** 174 | **10.** 132 | **11.** 474 | **12.** 684 |
| **E** | **1.** 1100 | **2.** 1600 | **3.** 600 | **4.** 400 | **5.** 280 | **6.** 120 |
| | **7.** 315 | **8.** 315 | **9.** 700 | **10.** 260 | **11.** 900 | **12.** 300 |
| | **13.** 300 | **14.** 2200 | **15.** 1300 | **16.** 330 | | |

*page 74*  **Mental arithmetic tests**

*Test 1*
**1.** 28  **2.** 292  **3.** 500  **4.** 54  **5.** 8006
**6.** $\frac{7}{10}$  **7.** 750 cm  **8.** 4600  **9.** 6  **10.** 74%
**11.** 25 cm$^2$  **12.** 7·25  **13.** −5°C  **14.** 20  **15.** Any of 3, 9, 27
**16.** 600  **17.** 64  **18.** 20  **19.** 2·2  **20.** £40
**21.** 13  **22.** 60  **23.** £6·80  **24.** 18  **25.** 5

*Test 2*

| | | | | |
|---|---|---|---|---|
| **1.** 36 | **2.** 24 | **3.** 6 | **4.** 60 | **5.** 75% |
| **6.** 1·3 | **7.** 35 | **8.** £8 | **9.** 50p, 10p, 5p, 2p | **10.** 180 |
| **11.** $\frac{5}{7}$ | **12.** £13·98 | **13.** 25 | **14.** 14 | **15.** 75p |
| **16.** 84p | **17.** 15p | **18.** 36p | **19.** 14 | **20.** £11·95 |
| **21.** 12 | **22.** 6 cm | **23.** £5·50 | **24.** 10 000 mm | **25.** 0530 |

*Test 3*

| | | | | |
|---|---|---|---|---|
| **1.** 32 cm | **2.** 20% | **3.** 4·5 | **4.** £1·27 | **5.** 5 weeks |
| **6.** £2 | **7.** 14p | **8.** 77p | **9.** 17 | **10.** 25·5 |
| **11.** 50 mins | **12.** 240 miles | **13.** £6·50 | **14.** $\frac{4}{7}$ | **15.** 41 mins |

**16.** 50, 5, 5, 1, 1, or 20, 20, 20, 1, 1 or 20, 20, 10, 10, 2

| | | | | |
|---|---|---|---|---|
| **17.** 50 006 | **18.** 13 | **19.** 450 cm | **20.** 132 | **21.** 0·6 |
| **22.** £50 | **23.** £7·03 | **24.** 6 | **25.** 165 mins | |

*Test 4*

| | | | | |
|---|---|---|---|---|
| **1.** 74 | **2.** 120° | **3.** 95° | **4.** £22 | **5.** 200 |
| **6.** £8380 | **7.** 138 | **8.** 28% | **9.** 38 | **10.** £6·45 |
| **11.** 20p, 10p, 10p, 10p, 1p | | **12.** 124 | **13.** 0·05 | **14.** 125 mins |
| **15.** 60 000 | **16.** Thursday | **17.** True | **18.** 3500 mm | **19.** £1·95 |
| **20.** 0·75 | **21.** 3600 | **22.** 83 | **23.** 150 cm$^2$ | **24.** 17 |
| **25.** 5 | | | | |

*Test 5*

| | | | | |
|---|---|---|---|---|
| **1.** 2·2 kg | **2.** 2000 | **3.** 10 000 cm$^2$ | **4.** £292 | **5.** 82° |
| **6.** £500 | **7.** 7·55 | **8.** £5 | **9.** £6·50 | **10.** 20 hours |
| **11.** 499 mm | **12.** 115 | **13.** 150 mins | **14.** 58 | **15.** 8·35 |
| **16.** 96 miles | **17.** 56 cm | **18.** 195 cm | **19.** 2 | **20.** 1935 |
| **21.** 300 mm | **22.** £100 | **23.** 52·5 | | |

**24.** 50p, 5p, 5p, 5p, 1p or 20p, 20p, 20p, 5p, 1p          **25.** Jim

*Test 6*

| | | | | |
|---|---|---|---|---|
| **1.** 8990 | **2.** £18 | **3.** 10 | **4.** 1020 | **5.** $2\frac{1}{2}$ |
| **6.** False | **7.** 20 cm$^2$ | **8.** 3·75 | **9.** 13 | **10.** 23 |
| **11.** 0·07 | **12.** 1·69 m | **13.** 360 m | **14.** 3 squared | **15.** 16 |
| **16.** 2 500 000 | **17.** £5·32 | **18.** 0·24 | **19.** 27 | **20.** 37 |
| **21.** 25 cm | **22.** 4 | **23.** $\frac{1}{8}$ | **24.** 60 000 | **25.** 12 |

*page 78* **Mathematical puzzles**

Part A

| | | | | | | | |
|---|---|---|---|---|---|---|---|
| ¹5 | 4 | ²2 | | ³1 | 5 | 1 | ⁴2 |
| 7 | | 3 | ⁵5 | 6 | | 1 | |
| | ⁶4 | 5 | ⁷7 | 1 | | ⁸9 | 6 |
| ⁹7 | 3 | | 4 | | ¹⁰3 | 1 | |
| 9 | | ¹¹2 | 8 | 4 | | 8 | ¹²5 |
| 9 | | 5 | | ¹³5 | ¹⁴8 | | 8 |
| ¹⁵7 | ¹⁶2 | 6 | 8 | | ¹⁷2 | 6 | 9 |
| | 1 | | ¹⁸2 | 1 | 1 | | 3 |

Part B

| | | | | | | | |
|---|---|---|---|---|---|---|---|
| ¹9 | 9 | ²0 | | ³9 | 9 | 1 | ⁴0 |
| 2 | | 2 | ⁵5 | 6 | | 0 | |
| | ⁶4 | 6 | ⁷8 | 4 | | ⁸0 | 1 |
| ⁹8 | 6 | | 2 | | ¹⁰6 | 0 | |
| 2 | | ¹¹8 | 0 | 8 | | 3 | ¹²2 |
| 4 | | 5 | | ¹³9 | ¹⁴7 | | 3 |
| ¹⁵2 | ¹⁶3 | 4 | 3 | | ¹⁷3 | 5 | 3 |
| | 7 | | ¹⁸2 | 2 | 5 | | 1 |

## Part C

| | | | | | | | |
|---|---|---|---|---|---|---|---|
| ¹1 | 6 | ²9 | ▓ | ³5 | 2 | 0 | ⁴0 |
| 8 | ▓ | 2 | ▓ | ⁵2 | 1 | ▓ | 6 |
| ▓ | ⁶1 | 2 | ⁷3 | 4 | ▓ | ⁸1 | 6 |
| ⁹3 | 6 | ▓ | 6 | ▓ | ¹⁰8 | 1 | ▓ |
| 6 | ▓ | ¹¹7 | 2 | 0 | ▓ | 0 | ¹²2 |
| 0 | ▓ | 5 | ▓ | ¹³1 | ¹⁴6 | ▓ | 3 |
| ¹⁵0 | ¹⁶2 | 3 | 4 | ▓ | ¹⁷0 | 0 | 4 |
| ▓ | 8 | ▓ | ¹⁸1 | 0 | 0 | ▓ | 5 |

## Part D

| | | | | | | | |
|---|---|---|---|---|---|---|---|
| ¹8 | 2 | ²8 | ▓ | ³8 | 0 | 0 | ⁴0 |
| 1 | ▓ | 3 | ▓ | ⁵3 | 6 | ▓ | 0 |
| ▓ | ⁶1 | 2 | ⁷1 | 0 | ▓ | ⁸8 | 4 |
| ⁹2 | 4 | ▓ | 0 | ▓ | ¹⁰6 | 6 | ▓ |
| 2 | ▓ | ¹¹0 | 0 | 5 | ▓ | 4 | ¹²4 |
| 4 | ▓ | 9 | ▓ | ¹³6 | ¹⁴4 | ▓ | 4 |
| ¹⁵1 | ¹⁶9 | 9 | 8 | ▓ | ¹⁷1 | 4 | 4 |
| ▓ | 0 | ▓ | ¹⁸3 | 7 | 1 | ▓ | 4 |

*page 80* **Puzzles**

**1.** (a) A = 4, B = 8, C = 11, D = 7       (b) A = 6, B = 2, C = 5, D = 4, E = 8
     (c) A = 6, B = 3, C = 1, D = 5       (d) A = 8, B = 3

**2.** (a)

(b)
(c)

(d)

(e)

(f)

**3.** 12

**4.**

| E | C | A | D | B |
|---|---|---|---|---|
| D | B | E | C | A |
| C | A | D | B | E |
| B | E | C | A | D |
| A | D | B | E | C |

**5.** 11 tapes at £7·99: £87·89

**6.**
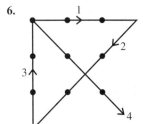

**7.**
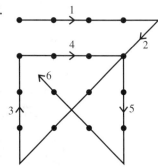

**8.** Three on each side etc!

9.

$$\boxed{9} - \boxed{5} = \boxed{4}$$

$$\boxed{6} \div \boxed{3} = \boxed{2}$$

$$\boxed{1} + \boxed{7} = \boxed{8}$$

10. (a) M = 2, E = 1, A = 4 or M = 4, E = 2, A = 8
    (b) K = 1, L = 8, M = 5
    (c) E = 0, V = 5, A = 3, S = 8; N, W, R = 1, 2, 4 in any order

11. (a) many solutions  (b) many solutions  (c) S = 1, O = 3, N = 9, U = 4, W = 0, I = 2
    (d) 1 2 4 5      or      2 3 4 5        (e) 2 9 8 0
        3 2 4 5              1 3 4 5             2 1 7 6+
        5 2 6 5+            5 3 6 5+             5 1 5 6
        9 7 5 5             9 0 5 5

# Part 3

*page 83*  **Exercise 1**

1. 1, 2, 3, 6
2. 1, 2, 4
3. 1, 2, 5, 10
4. 1, 7
5. 1, 3, 5, 15
6. 1, 2, 3, 6, 9, 18
7. 1, 2, 3, 4, 6, 8, 12, 24
8. 1, 3, 7, 21
9. 1, 2, 3, 4, 6, 9, 12, 18, 36
10. 1, 2, 4, 5, 8, 10, 20, 40
11. 1, 2, 4, 8, 16, 32
12. 1, 31
13. 1, 2, 3, 4, 5, 6, 10, 12, 15, 20, 30, 60
14. 1, 3, 7, 9, 21, 63
15. 1, 5, 17, 85
16. (d) prime factors are $2 \times 2 \times 3 \times 3$
17. $2 \times 2 \times 7$
18. $2 \times 2 \times 2 \times 2 \times 2$
19. $2 \times 17$
20. $3 \times 3 \times 3 \times 3$
21. $2 \times 2 \times 3 \times 7$
22. $2 \times 2 \times 2 \times 3 \times 3 \times 3$
23. $2 \times 3 \times 7 \times 7$
24. $2 \times 2 \times 2 \times 5 \times 5$
25. $2 \times 2 \times 3 \times 5 \times 5 \times 5$
26. $2 \times 2 \times 2 \times 2 \times 2 \times 7 \times 11$
27. $2 \times 2 \times 3 \times 5 \times 7 \times 11$
28. $3 \times 5 \times 5 \times 7 \times 11 \times 17$
31. 64 or 96
32. 210 ($2 \times 3 \times 5 \times 7$)
33. 2520 ($= 2^3 \times 3^2 \times 5 \times 7$)

*page 84*  **Exercise 2**

1. 3, 6, 9, 12
2. 4, 8, 12, 16
3. 2, 4, 6, 8
4. 7, 14, 21, 28
5. 10, 20, 30, 40
6. 5, 10, 15, 20, 25, 30
7. 8, 16, 24, 32, 40, 48
8. 9, 18, 27, 36, 45, 54
9. 11, 22, 33, 44, 55, 66
10. 20, 40, 60, 80, 100, 120
11. (a) 4  (b) 5  (c) 7
12. 32
13. 101
14. 5
15. 56
16. 18
17. 12, 24, 36
18. 10, 20, 30
19. 30, 60, 90
20. 48, 96 or 12, 24

*page 85*  **Exercise 3**

1. (a) 2, 4, 6, 8      (b) 5, 10, 15, 20      (c) 10
2. (a) 4, 8, 12, 16    (b) 12, 24, 36, 48    (c) 12
3. (a) 18      (b) 24      (c) 70      (d) 12      (e) 30      (f) 252
4. 12
5. (a) 6      (b) 11      (c) 9      (d) 6      (e) 12      (f) 10
6. 66            7. 195

*page 86*   ***Exercise 4***

**1.** (a) 25, 36, 49, 64          **2.** (a) 25    (b) 64    (c) 100    (d) 1
**3.** (a) 25    (b) 14    (c) 181      **4.** $3^2$, $4^2$, $5^2$, $6^2$ etc                    **5.** (a) 7    (b) 9    (c) 12
**6.** (a) 5    (b) 9    (c) 7    (d) 1    **7.** (a) 7    (b) 14    (c) 441    (d) 10·89
**8.** (a) $1 + 9$            (b) $16 + 4 + 4$        (c) $36 + 9 + 1 + 1$    (d) $64 + 1 + 1$        (e) $81 + 16 + 1$
   (f) $49 + 9 + 4 + 1$    (g) $100 + 16 + 4$    (h) $121 + 16 + 4$    (i) $225 + 196 + 1 + 1$
**9.** $13 + 15 + 17 + 19 = 64 = 4^3$                    $21 + 23 + 25 + 27 + 29 = 125 = 5^3$
   $31 + 33 + 35 + 37 + 39 + 41 = 216 = 6^3$
**10.** (a) 14        (b) 16        (c) 24        (d) 44        (e) 195
**11.** ×3                **12.** ×5

*page 88*   ***Exercise 5***

**1.** (a) 17, 29        (b) 41, 67        (c) 2, 71
**3.** All the prime numbers in columns A and B can be written as the sum of two square numbers.
**4.** The pattern does continue.
**5.** $2 + 3 = 5$, $2 + 5 = 7$, $2 + 17 = 19$ (many others)
**6.** one                **7.** $3 + 5 + 11 = 19$ (many others)

*page 89*   ***Exercise 6***

**1.** 293, 709, 1009 are prime.
**2.** (a) 7 hours 12 minutes 42 seconds        (b) 18 pages (17·3 actually)

*page 90*   ***Satisfied numbers*** (other solutions are possible)

**1.**

|  | Number between 5 and 9 | Square number | Prime number |
|---|---|---|---|
| Factor of 6 | 6 | 1 | 3 |
| Even number | 8 | 4 | 2 |
| Odd number | 7 | 9 | 5 |

**2.**

|  | Prime number | Multiple of 3 | Factor of 16 |
|---|---|---|---|
| Number greater than 5 | 7 | 9 | 8 |
| Odd number | 5 | 3 | 1 |
| Even number | 2 | 6 | 4 |

**3.** Many solutions

*page 91*   ***Happy numbers***

The Happy numbers are:- 1, 7, 10, 13, 19, 23, 28, 31, 32, 44, 49, 68, 70, 79, 82, 86, 91, 94, 97, 100
Encourage pupils to find 'short cuts'. E.g. if 23 is happy, so is 32.

*page 93*   **Exercise 1**

| | | | | | | | |
|---|---|---|---|---|---|---|---|
| **1.** 11 | **2.** 1 | **3.** −5 | **4.** 12 | **5.** 21 | **6.** 2 | **7.** 17 | **8.** 24 |
| **9.** 9 | **10.** 30 | **11.** 30 | **12.** 25 | **13.** 8 | **14.** 5 | **15.** 6 | **16.** 8 |
| **17.** 8 | **18.** 3 | **19.** 7 | **20.** −2 | **21.** −4 | **22.** 14 | **23.** 13 | **24.** 0 |
| **25.** 52 | **26.** 11 | **27.** 10 | **28.** 20 | **29.** 5 | **30.** 5 | | |

*page 93*   **Exercise 2**

| | | | | | | | |
|---|---|---|---|---|---|---|---|
| **1.** 15 | **2.** 10 | **3.** 5 | **4.** 9 | **5.** 11 | **6.** 1 | **7.** 7 | **8.** 8 |
| **9.** 8 | **10.** 4 | **11.** 0 | **12.** 1 | **13.** 18 | **14.** 18 | **15.** 12 | **16.** 27 |
| **17.** 8 | **18.** 6 | **19.** 1 | **20.** 22 | **21.** 9 | **22.** 0 | **23.** 5 | **24.** 0 |
| **25.** 20 | **26.** 10 | **27.** 16 | **28.** 52 | **29.** 40 | **30.** 111 | **31.** 51 | **32.** 30 |
| **33.** 11 | **34.** 9 | **35.** 28 | **36.** 106 | **37.** 54 | **38.** 4 | **39.** 4 | **40.** 153 |
| **41.** 59 | **42.** 165 | **43.** 85 | **44.** 12 | **45.** 33 | **46.** 64 | **47.** 67 | **48.** 1172 |
| **49.** 52 | **50.** 5 | **51.** 4 | **52.** 16 | **53.** 8 | **54.** 2 | | |

*page 94*   **Exercise 3**

| | | | | | | | |
|---|---|---|---|---|---|---|---|
| **1.** 16 | **2.** 27 | **3.** 0 | **4.** 37 | **5.** 8 | **6.** 7 | **7.** 12 | **8.** 64 |
| **9.** 80 | **10.** 18 | **11.** 496 | **12.** 125 | **13.** 81 | **14.** 8 | **16.** 27 | **16.** 1 |
| **17.** 64 | **18.** 64 | **19.** 16 | **20.** 10 | **21.** 18 | **22.** 40 | **23.** 24 | **24.** 4 |

*page 95*   **Exercise 4**

**1.** $(3 + 4) \times 5 = 35$
**2.** $6 + (9 \times 7) = 69$
**3.** $(7 \times 2) + 3 = 17$
**4.** $(9 + 12) \times 5 = 105$
**5.** $6 \times (8 - 2) = 36$
**6.** $(3 \times 8) - 6 = 18$
**7.** $(19 - 6) \times 3 = 39$
**8.** $27 - (9 \div 3) = 24$
**9.** $(51 \div 3) + 4 = 21$
**10.** $7 \times (24 - 5) = 133$
**11.** $(6 + 14) \div 2 = 10$
**12.** $(11 + 6) \times 4 = 68$
**13.** $(12 \times 8) - (9 \times 7) = 33$
**14.** $(8 \times 9) - (4 \times 7) = 44$
**15.** $(5 \times 6 - 4) \div 2 = 13$
**16.** $(81 \div 9) \times (12 - 4) = 72$
**17.** $(3 + 5) \times (9 - 7) = 16$
**18.** $(16 - 10) \div (18 \div 6) = 2$
**19.** $(6 + 7 - 1) \div 2 = 6$
**20.** $(5 + 7) \div 3 \times 0 = 0$

*page 95*   **Exercise 5**

**1.** $(4 + 8) \div 2 = 6$
**2.** $(5 + 2) \times 3 = 21$
**3.** $(7 + 2) \div 3 = 3$
**4.** $(9 - 4) + 2 = 7$
**5.** $(8 - 4) \times 5 = 20$
**6.** $(20 - 2) \div 3 = 6$
**7.** $(7 \times 4) + 2 = 30$
**8.** $(7 \times 6) - 22 = 20$
**9.** $(6 \div 3) \times 4 = 8$
**10.** $40 \div (8 - 3) = 8$
**11.** $(36 + 4) \div 8 = 5$
**12.** $(49 \div 7) \times 2 = 14$
**13.** $21 + 14 - 11 = 24$
**14.** $(16 \times 3) + 9 = 57$
**15.** $(12 + 16) \div 4 = 7$
**16.** $42 + 6 - 24 = 24$
**17.** $(18 - 13) \times 5 = 25$
**18.** $40 \div (16 - 6) = 4$
**19.** $(7 \times 8) - 6 = 50$
**20.** $(13 \times 4) - 8 = 44$
**21.** $4 \times (9 \div 3) = 12$
**22.** $7 \times (9 \div 3) = 21$
**23.** $(45 \div 3) - 4 = 11$
**24.** $(121 \div 11) \times 7 = 77$

*page 96*   **Exercise 1**

**1.** (a) £6·10   (b) £6·40   (c) £4·70   (d) £116   (e) £129·30   (f) £0·04
**2.** (a) 2·5   (b) 4·25   (c) 3·75   (d) 0·1   (e) 0·2   (f) 0·9
   (g) 5·4   (h) 1·33 (1·$\dot{3}$)   (i) 3·66 (3·$\dot{6}$)
**3.** (a) 24 h 45 min   (b) 30 h   (c) 2 h 54 min   (d) 6 h   (e) 9 h 54 min   (f) 17 h 24 min
**4.** (a) 7 h 15 min   (b) 16 h 20 min   (c) 22 h 30 min   (d) 2 h 24 min   (e) 3 h 36 min   (f) 7 h 40 min

*page 97*   *Exercise 2*

| | | | | | |
|---|---|---|---|---|---|
| **1.** 4·2 | **2.** 15·9 | **3.** 0·6 | **4.** 5·3 | **5.** 4·0 | **6.** 12·7 |
| **7.** 0·5 | **8.** 5·6 | **9.** 14·0 | **10.** 3·4 | **11.** 4·4 | **12.** 0·7 |
| **13.** 9·9 | **14.** 9·1 | **15.** 9·5 | **16.** 0·6 | **17.** 23·0 | **18.** 11·4 |
| **19.** 7·4 | **20.** 5·5 | **21.** 11·5 | **22.** 11·7 | **23.** 10·9 | **24.** 1·9 |
| **25.** 13·0 | **26.** 4·9 | **27.** 18·8 | **28.** 3·4 | **29.** 2·4 | **30.** 2·9 |

*page 98*   *Exercise 3*

| | | | | | |
|---|---|---|---|---|---|
| **1.** 9·05 | **2.** 11·38 | **3.** 4·91 | **4.** 12·4 | **5.** 1·47 | **6.** 4·68 |
| **7.** 2·20 | **8.** 2·61 | **9.** 0·74 | **10.** 1·41 | **11.** 3·71 | **12.** 15·11 |
| **13.** 9·28 | **14.** 10·02 | **15.** 5·98 | **16.** 6·90 | **17.** 0·97 | **18.** 0·21 |
| **19.** 5·36 | **20.** 80·60 | **21.** 7·77 | **22.** 16·56 | **23.** 7·34 | **24.** 12·51 |
| **25.** 64·11 | **26.** 1·58 | **27.** 14·09 | **28.** 2·49 | **29.** 0·59 | **30.** 2·70 |
| **31.** 86·65 | **32.** 44·91 | **33.** 1·04 | **34.** 1·03 | **35.** 6·27 | **36.** 0·83 |
| **37.** 2·33 | **38.** 9·89 | **39.** 13·38 | **40.** 1·52 | | |

*page 99*   *Exercise 4*

| | | | | |
|---|---|---|---|---|
| **1.** OI | **2.** IGLOO | **3.** BOILED | **4.** EGGS | **5.** SELL |
| **6.** I | **7.** SIGHED | **8.** HEIDI | **9.** SHELLS | **10.** BIG |
| **11.** GOOSE | **12.** EGGS | **13.** GEESE | **14.** SIEGE | **15.** SID |
| **16.** HE | **17.** IS | **18.** BIG | **19.** SLOB | **20.** LESLIE |
| **21.** HE | **22.** SLOSHED | **23.** BOOZE | **24.** OH | **25.** BOSS |
| **26.** HEDGEHOG | | | | |

*page 100*   *Exercise 5*

| | | | | | |
|---|---|---|---|---|---|
| **1.** 5·17 | **2.** 1·69 | **3.** 2·11 | **4.** 0·49 | **5.** 4·26 | **6.** 0·64 |
| **7.** 11·79 | **8.** 2·78 | **9.** 10·98 | **10.** 1·23 | **11.** 7·87 | **12.** 7·73 |
| **13.** 2·19 | **14.** 1·32 | **15.** 1·87 | **16.** 7·46 | **17.** 28·84 | **18.** 13·27 |
| **19.** 70·19 | **20.** 30·14 | **21.** 14·89 | **22.** 0·19 | **23.** 0·31 | **24.** 9·28 |
| **25.** 1·16 | **26.** 20·40 | **27.** 1·33 | **28.** 1·16 | **29.** 2·52 | **30.** 1·20 |
| **31.** 10·28 | **32.** 2·33 | **33.** 8·26 | **34.** 15·31 | **35.** 4·73 | **36.** 66·24 |

*page 102*   *Exercise 1*

| | | | | |
|---|---|---|---|---|
| **1.** 0·57 m | **2.** 1300 m | **3.** 240 g | **4.** 0·6 kg | **5.** 1·7 cm |
| **6.** 3 t | **7.** 60 cm | **8.** 1·4 cm | **9.** 2 $\ell$ | **10.** 0·305 |
| **11.** 0·8 m | **12.** 0·2 m | **13.** 2500 kg | **14.** 2400 mm | **15.** 0·02 kg |
| **16.** 4500 ml | **17.** 2000 cm$^3$ | **18.** 550 cm | **19.** 0·056 m | **20.** 0·007 kg |
| **21.** 36 inches | **22.** 15 feet | **23.** 32 ounces | **24.** 126 pounds | **25.** 2 feet |
| **26.** 8 ounces | **27.** 30 inches | **28.** 2240 pounds | **29.** 116 pounds | **30.** 62 inches |
| **31.** 32 g | **32.** 2 yards | **33.** $\frac{1}{2}$ pound | **34.** 5280 feet | **35.** 23·5 cm |
| **36.** 420 kg | **37.** 0·111 m | **38.** 4 ounces | **39.** 7000 ml | **40.** 12 feet |
| **41.** 0·7 cm | **42.** 16 pints | **43.** 0·4 km | **44.** 40 pints | **45.** 17 600 yards |

*page 103*  **Exercise 2**

**1.** 6 feet          **2.** 60 g          **3.** 60 miles          **4.** 25 g          **5.** 3 mm
**6.** 30 m          **7.** 500 ml          **8.** 10 mm          **9.** (c) or a large van!
**10.** (a) 365     (b) 5025     (c) 4300 g [error: should be 0·4 kg]     (d) 55     (e) 6·6     (f) 7·18

*page 103*  **Exercise 3**

**1.** (a) 6 pounds     **2.** 25 cm          **3.** 20 litres          **4.** 15 miles          **5.** 150 cm
**6.** 160 pounds     **7.** 10 cm          **8.** 50 litres          **9.** 185 cm          **10.** Yes
**11.** 10 pounds     **12.** £12/£10     **13.** 50 m.p.h.     **14.** 25 miles
**15.** (a) 3 kg     (b) 15 litres     (c) 3 pounds     **16.** $\frac{1}{2}$ inch     **17.** £20     **18.** 90

*page 105*  **Exercise 4**

**1.** (a) 1·98 m$^2$     (b) 0·07 m$^2$     (c) 2·92 m$^2$          **2.** 400
**3.** 4·24 kg                    **4.** 4·5 g                    **5.** 0·125 mm                    **6.** 5600
**7.** 14                    **8.** 725·76 litres          **9.** (a) 19 800 cm$^2$     (b) 4800 cm$^2$     (c) 0·48 cm$^2$
**10.** (a) 276 hectares     (b) 23 hours          **11.** 0·6 seconds
**12.** (a) 100 000 000 000     (b) £20 000 000 000 [i.e. £20 billion!]

*page 108*  **Exercise 3**

**1.** (a) $\frac{1}{2}$   (b) $\frac{1}{4}$   (c) 100 g     **2.** (a) $\frac{1}{4}$   (b) $\frac{1}{8}$   (c) 10     **3.** 120°

**4.**

| Method | car | walk | train | bus |
|---|---|---|---|---|
| Number of people | 40 | 10 | 20 | 10 |

**5.** (a) £6·00          (b) £6·00          (c) £3·00          (d) £4·00          (e) £3·00          (f) £2·00
**6.** (a) (i) 120     (ii) 135          (b) 18°          (c) 30
**7.** (a) 36 g     (b) 1 g = 10°     (c) Oats 60°, Barley 90°, Sugar 30°, Rye 180°

**8.**

| Programme | Angle |
|---|---|
| News | 40° |
| Soap | 100° |
| Comedy | 80° |
| Drama | 100° |
| Film | 40° |

**9.**

| Sport | Angle |
|---|---|
| Rugby | 75° |
| Football | 105° |
| Tennis | 60° |
| Squash | 30° |
| Athletics | 45° |
| Swimming | 45° |

**10.**

| Subject | Angle |
|---|---|
| Maths | 45° |
| English | 45° |
| Science | 54° |
| Humanities | 36° |
| Arts | 36° |
| Others | 144° |

**11.** 1 meal = 3°     **12.** (a) $\frac{1}{3}$   (b) 30 children     (c) 18 children
**14.** (a) 15%     (b) $x = 126°$   $y = 109°$
**15.** (a) 5 → 10%     (b) About 150     (c) There were more people on the ferry

*page 111*  **Exercise 2**

**1.** (a) football          (b) 5          (c) 25
**2.** (a) 18          (b) £1·50          (c) Prawn
**3.** (a) 40          (b) 10          (c) 40          (d) Belair
**4.** (a) C          (b) D          (c) B          (d) A
**5.** (a) 10          (b) 80          (c) you cannot have $\frac{1}{2}$ bedroom
**6.** (a) England and Wales          (b) 50          (c) very low rate (1 person)
      (d) about 6 times more likely          (e) for discussion

*page 114* **Exercise 3**

**1.** (a) Frequencies: 2, 5, 7, 4, 3
**2.** (a) Frequencies: 10, 6, 1, 0, 2, 4, 6, 5
  (c) Because it is not entirely concerned with 7 year olds. It includes parents
  (d) Should look more like question **1**.
**3.** Yes
**4.** There were more heavy pigs using the new diet
**5.** Theory was not correct. Those who watched most T.V. did *better* in the tests than they did before. The results of the other group were neither better nor worse than before.
**6.** (a) 10          (b) 24          (c) 34
**7.** (a) 4/5%          (b) 11%          (c) (i) 4/5%     (ii) 0·5%
  (d) Far more old people in U.K. (Better health care, diet etc.)
  (e) Kenya half male, half female. Saudi Arabia significantly more males

*page 120* **Mid-book review** **Exercise 1**

**1.** (a) 3     (b) 15          **2.** (a) $728 \div 4 = 182$     (b) $87 \div 3 = 29$
**3.** 80                    **4.** 10 000          **5.** (a) 2 h 30 min     (b) 3 h 35 min     (c) 4 h 10 min
**6.** T          **7.** F          **8.** T          **9.** T          **10.** T
**11.** F          **12.** T          **13.** T          **14.** F          **15.** C
**16.** (a) 107     (b) 4·0.     (c) 1·9     (d) $\frac{5}{8}$
**17.** (a) $1 \to 4 \to 13 \to 40$          (b) $2 \to 7 \to 22 \to 67$          (c) $\frac{1}{3} \to 2 \to 7 \to 22$
**18.** (a) 27     (b) 0·5     (c) 7
**19.** (c) cone, tetrahedron, cube, cylinder, cuboid, sphere
**20.** equilateral          **21.** isosceles          **22.** scalene          **23.** square
**24.** True          **25.** hemisphere          **26.** False
**27.** (a) CB     (b) JK     (c) H     **28.** (a) 55 600     (b) 300     (c) 700     (d) 44 000
**29.** (a) 3·6     (b) 0·8     (c) 11·3     (d) 8·0
**30.** B                    **31.** he was wrong, 12 years is about 105 120 hours
**32.** (a) 34 m$^2$     (b) 26 m          **33.** 16 cm$^2$

*page 122* **Exercise 2**

**1.** (a) $\frac{4}{7}$     (b) $\frac{1}{8}$     (c) $\frac{9}{12} = \frac{3}{4}$     (d) $\frac{8}{15}$          **2.** $\frac{3}{4}$ is larger than $\frac{2}{3}$
**3.** (a) £9          (b) £3·60     (c) £12     (d) £4          (e) £0·96     (f) £750
**4.** £31·50
**5.** (3, −2) (1, −3) (0, −1) (−2, −2) (−2, −1) (−1, −1) (−2, −1) (−2, 0) (−3, 0) (−2, 2) (−1, 2) (−1, 1)
  (−2, 2) (−2, 3) (−3, 3) (−4, 4) (−2, 5) (0, 5) (2, 4) (3, 3) (3, 1) (2, 3) (0, 4) (−1, 4) (−2, 3)
**6.** (a) (9, 7)          (b) (4, 3)
**7.** (a) parallelogram     (b) trapezium     (c) kite     (d) isosceles triangle     (e) square
**8.** (a) $2x + 5$     (b) $3n - 7$     (c) $\dfrac{4t + 1}{2}$          **9.** $3a + 12, 2n + 2m$
**11.** (a) $6a + 2b$     (b) $4n + 4m$     (c) $3a + 1$
**12.** (a) $5n - 3$     (b) A and D     (c) C     (d) $7n + 3$
**13.** (a) 97     (b) 146     (c) 148     (d) 1200     (e) 256     (f) 66

*page 124* **Exercise 3**

**1.** 7, 14, 21, 28, 35, 42          **2.** (a) 1, 2, 3, 6, 9, 18     (b) 1, 3, 9, 27
**3.** (a) 27     (b) 39          **4.** (a) 6, 12, 18, 24, 30     (b) 8, 16, 24, 32, 40
**5.** (a) 23     (b) 47          **6.** (b) 6          **7.** Many answers, e.g. 30

**8.** $2 \times 2 \times 3 \times 5 \times 7 \times 7$, Not square number    **9.** clockwise from top: 11, 7, 4; 5, 9, 7

**10.** (a) 10    (b) 3    (c) 26    (d) 19    (e) 18    (f) 34

**11.** (a) 11·0    (b) 5·1    (c) 7·8    (d) 24·1    (e) 1·4    (f) 3·2

**12.** (a) +    (b) −    (c) −4 + 1

**13.** 84 000 beats      **14.** C

---

*page 126*    **Operator squares**

**1.**

| 15 | ÷ | 3 | → | 5 |
|----|---|---|---|-----|
| + |  | × |  |  |
| 22 | × | 5 | → | 110 |
| ↓ |  | ↓ |  |  |
| 37 | − | 15 | → | 22 |

**2.**

| 14 | + | 17 | → | 31 |
|----|---|----|---|----|
| × |  | + |  |  |
| 4 | × | 23 | → | 92 |
| ↓ |  | ↓ |  |  |
| 56 | − | 40 | → | 16 |

**3.**

| 13 | × | 4 | → | 52 |
|----|---|---|---|------|
| − |  | + |  |  |
| 5 | ÷ | 4 | → | 1.25 |
| ↓ |  | ↓ |  |  |
| 8 | ÷ | 8 | → | 1 |

**4.**

| 17 | × | 10 | → | 170 |
|----|---|-----|---|-----|
| − |  | ÷ |  |  |
| 9 | × | 100 | → | 900 |
| ↓ |  | ↓ |  |  |
| 8 | − | 0.1 | → | 7.9 |

**5.**

| 38 | × | 8 | → | 304 |
|----|---|-----|---|-----|
| ÷ |  | × |  |  |
| 2 | × | 14 | → | 28 |
| ↓ |  | ↓ |  |  |
| 19 | + | 112 | → | 131 |

**6.**

| 2106 | − | 574 | → | 1532 |
|------|---|-----|---|------|
| ÷ |  | + |  |  |
| 9 | × | 25 | → | 225 |
| ↓ |  | ↓ |  |  |
| 234 | + | 599 | → | 833 |

**7.**

| 10 | × | 0.1 | → | 1 |
|----|---|------|---|------|
| ÷ |  | × |  |  |
| 4 | × | 0.2 | → | 0.8 |
| ↓ |  | ↓ |  |  |
| 2.5 | + | 0.02 | → | 2.52 |

**8.**

| 19.6 | ÷ | 7 | → | 2.8 |
|------|---|-----|---|------|
| × |  | − |  |  |
| 0.1 | ÷ | 0.1 | → | 1 |
| ↓ |  | ↓ |  |  |
| 1.96 | + | 6.9 | → | 8.86 |

**9.**

| 8.42 | × | 0.2 | → | 1.684 |
|------|---|------|---|--------|
| × |  | × |  |  |
| 100 | × | 0.3 | → | 30 |
| ↓ |  | ↓ |  |  |
| 842 | + | 0.06 | → | 842.06 |

**10.**

| 20 | − | 0.1 | → | 19.9 |
|----|---|------|---|------|
| × |  | − |  |  |
| 20 | × | 0.01 | → | 0.2 |
| ↓ |  | ↓ |  |  |
| 400 | × | 0.09 | → | 36 |

**11.**

| 1.22 | × | 3 | → | 3.66 |
|------|---|-----|---|------|
| + |  | − |  |  |
| 3.78 | + | 0.2 | → | 3.98 |
| ↓ |  | ↓ |  |  |
| 5 | + | 2.8 | → | 7.8 |

**12.**

| 328 | + | 578 | → | 906 |
|-----|---|-----|---|-------|
| ÷ |  | − |  |  |
| 20 | × | 52 | → | 1040 |
| ↓ |  | ↓ |  |  |
| 16.4 | + | 526 | → | 542.4 |

**13.**

| 4.6 | + | 5.3 | → | 9.9 |
|-----|---|------|---|-----|
| + | | × | | |
| 0.4 | × | 1000 | → | 400 |
| ↓ | | ↓ | | |
| 5 | + | 5300 | → | 5305 |

**14.**

| 1962 | ÷ | 18 | → | 109 |
|------|---|------|---|------|
| + | | + | | |
| 40 | ÷ | 1000 | → | 0.04 |
| ↓ | | ↓ | | |
| 2002 | − | 1018 | → | 984 |

**15.**

| 650 | ÷ | 13 | → | 50 |
|------|---|------|---|------|
| ÷ | | ÷ | | |
| 20 | ÷ | 200 | → | 0.1 |
| ↓ | | ↓ | | |
| 32.5 | + | 0.065 | → | |

32.565

# Part 4

*page 128*  **Exercise 1**

**1.** 60°      **2.** 110°      **3.** 117°      **4.** 48°
**5.** 50°      **6.** 40°      **7.** 72°      **8.** 40°
**9.** 60°      **10.** 36°      **11.** 28°      **12.** $22\frac{1}{2}°$
**13.** 32°      **14.** 30°      **15.** 30°      **16.** 28°

*page 129*  **Exercise 2**

**1.** 70°      **2.** 190°      **3.** 165°      **4.** 85°
**5.** 68°      **6.** 72°      **7.** 60°      **8.** 59°
**9.** 35°      **10.** 254°      **11.** 210°      **12.** 338°

*page 131*  **Exercise 3**

**1.** 80°      **2.** 60°      **3.** 51°      **4.** 105°
**5.** 98°      **6.** 60°      **7.** 50°      **8.** $c = 65°$, $d = 50°$
**9.** $e = 58°$, $f = 64°$   **10.** $g = h = 63°$      **11.** $h = 92°$, $i = 88°$, $j = 42°$
**12.** $k = 72°$, $l = 72°$, $m = 36°$      **13.** $n = 72°$, $p = 54°$   **14.** 40°
**15.** 37°      **16.** 30°      **17.** 72°
**18.** 76°      **19.** $a = 40°$, $b = 60°$   **20.** $a = 105°$, $x = 30°$

*page 132*  **Exercise 4**

**1.** $a = 110°$, $b = 110°$, $c = 70°$      **2.** $d = e = 65°$, $f = 115°$
**3.** $g = h = 104°$, $i = 76°$      **4.** $k = 68°$, $l = m = 112°$
**5.** $n = O = 111°$      **6.** $a = 60°$, $b = 115°$, $c = 65°$
**7.** $d = 50°$, $e = 55°$, $f = 125°$      **8.** $p = 73°$, $q = 107°$, $r = 97°$, $s = 83°$
**9.** $s = 100°$, $t = u = 40°$      **10.** $v = 49°$, $w = 41°$
**11.** $a = 64°$, $b = 50°$, $c = 66°$      **12.** $d = 65°$, $e = 30°$, $f = 85°$

*page 133*  **Exercise 5**

**1.** 64°      **2.** 95°      **3.** 50°      **4.** 105°      **5.** $e = 72°$, $f = 100°$
**6.** 95°      **7.** 120°      **8.** 40, 80°      **9.** 100°      **10.** 110°      **11.** 80°
**12.** 69      **13.** 64°      **14.** $p = 85°$      **15.** $q = 36°$      **16.** 51°      **17.** 20°
**18.** 69°      **19.** 72°      **20.** 28°      **21.** 54°

*page 135* **Exercise 1**

**1.** (a) $\frac{1}{4}$   (b) $\frac{1}{8}$    **2.** $\frac{7}{30}$    **3.** $\frac{1}{5}$    **4.** About 60%    **5.** 750 ml

*page 136* **Exercise 2**

**1.** £28    **2.** £6    **3.** £3    **4.** 400    **5.** 10 min    **6.** £4·80
**7.** £84    **8.** 12 litres    **9.** 28 min    **10.** 3655 g    **11.** 400    **12.** 165 min
**13.** 11    **14.** 315    **15.** 8    **16.** 55 litres

*page 137* **Exercise 3**

**1.** 11 : 7    **2.** 5 : 1    **3.** 3 : 2
**4.** (a) 1 : 3    (b) 3 : 5    (c) 1 : 11    (d) 2 : 3 : 4    (e) 2 : 5    (f) 1 : 8
**5.** 40    **6.** 20    **7.** 20    **8.** 35
**9.** 12 knives, 15 spoons    **10.** (a) 8, 4    (b) 9, 6    (c) 5, 30
**11.** (a) 14, 21    (b) £36, £63    (c) £12, £27    (d) 24, 8, 12    (e) £32, £8, £40    (f) 28 m, 21 m, 7 m
**12.** Ben £14, Chris £7    **13.** £45    **14.** Ratio of 1 to 4 is a proportion of $\frac{1}{5}$    **15.** $\frac{1}{5}$

*page 139* **Exercise 1**

**1.** (a) 45°   (b) 135°    **2.** (a) 37°   (b) 143°    **3.** (a) 70°   (b) 48°   (c) 62°
**4.** (a) 30°   (b) 20°   (c) 130°    **5.** (a) 140°   (b) 100°    **6.** (a) 50°   (b) 90°   (c) 120°   (d) 100°

*page 140* **Exercise 2**

**1.** 20°    **2.** 40°    **3.** 60°    **4.** 72°    **5.** 10°    **6.** 45°    **7.** 65°    **8.** 80°    **9.** 36°
**10.** 23°    **11.** 14°    **12.** 28°    **13.** 126°    **14.** 135°    **15.** 170°    **16.** 6°    **17.** 30°    **18.** 174°
**19.** 166°    **20.** 160°    **21.** 157°    **22.** 150°    **23.** 144°    **24.** 53°    **25.** 115°    **26.** 155°    **27.** 97°
**28.** 108°    **29.** 120°    **30.** 127°    **31.** 25°    **32.** 83°    **33.** 91°    **34.** 107°    **35.** 140°    **36.** 54°
**37.** 73°    **38.** 89°    **39.** 152°    **40.** 100°

*page 140* **Exercise 3**

**1.** 30°    **2.** 50°    **3.** 104°    **4.** 76°    **5.** 76°    **6.** 127°

*page 141* **Exercise 4**

**1.** 35°    **2.** 38°    **3.** 43°    **4.** 133°    **5.** 112°    **6.** 24°    **7.** 111°    **8.** 45°
**9.** $94\frac{1}{2}°$    **10.** 122°    **11.** 100°    **12.** 66°    **13.** 102°    **14.** 24°    **15.** $45\frac{1}{2}°$    **16.** 65°

*page 142* **Exercise 6**

**1.** 7·0 cm    **2.** 7·0 cm    **3.** 7·4 cm    **4.** 15·0 cm    **5.** 11·3 cm    **6.** 7·0 cm
**7.** 9·4 cm    **8.** 9·2 cm    **9.** 5·3 cm    **10.** 5·9 cm    **11.** 10·8 cm    **12.** 14·1 cm

*page 143* **Exercise 7**

**1.** 57°    **2.** 29°    **3.** 84°    **4.** 91°    **5.** 40°    **6.** 40°    **7.** 98°    **8.** 64°    **9.** 50°
**10.** £389 000

*page 145*

KEEP THE PRICE DOWN    (a) About £3 660 000    (b) About £2 670 000

*page 146*    *Exercise 1*

**1.** 10·2        **2.** 6·9        **3.** 14·8        **4.** 28·0        **5.** 36·78      **6.** 71·54      **7.** 42·72      **8.** 11·61
**9.** 4·41       **10.** 8·712    **11.** 0·666    **12.** 56·5      **13.** 68         **14.** 0·37       **15.** 13·32     **16.** 92·4
**17.** (a) 1·2    (b) 7    (c) 0·4    (d) 0·2    (e) 0·5    (f) 0·02              **18.** £27·80    **19.** £21·90    **20.** 6·75 kg


*page 147*    *Exercise 2*

**1.** 4·21            **2.** 34·2            **3.** 4·63            **4.** 0·712          **5.** 47·2            **6.** 6·31
**7.** 6·24            **8.** 54·14          **9.** 1·34            **10.** £1·52         **11.** 5·63 cm       **12.** £8·47
**13.** (a) 2·24          (b) 2·2525          (c) 1·5125          (d) 0·205          (e) 3·4            (f) 2·75


*page 148*    *Exercise 3*

**1.** 42·3            **2.** 56·3            **3.** 42·7            **4.** 463            **5.** 0·75            **6.** 0·63
**7.** 1147           **8.** 10 700         **9.** 633            **10.** 71·4          **11.** 636           **12.** 81·42
**13.** 7100          **14.** 8900          **15.** 1200          **16.** 130           **17.** 0·24          **18.** 0·89
**19.** 0·63          **20.** 0·007         **21.** 0·086         **22.** 0·0516        **23.** 0·00077       **24.** 0·0219
**25.** 0·05          **26.** 0·0026        **27.** 0·00051       **28.** 89·04         **29.** 40·07         **30.** 0·02
**31.** 51·4          **32.** 626           **33.** 41·4          **34.** 63·1          **35.** 0·5           **36.** 63
**37.** 4·74          **38.** 0·0897        **39.** 0·0542        **40.** 6300          **41.** 470           **42.** 8400
**43.** 0·007         **44.** 0·62          **45.** 47·3          **46.** 1             **47.** 0·47          **48.** 4700


*page 149*    *Exercise 4*

**1.** 0·08           **2.** 0·18           **3.** 0·16           **4.** 0·012          **5.** 2·1            **6.** 0·014
**7.** 0·45           **8.** 0·24           **9.** 0 002          **10.** 0·49          **11.** 0·8           **12.** 4·2
**13.** 0·45          **14.** 0·016         **15.** 0·0006        **16.** 0·66          **17.** 0·36          **18.** 0·64
**19.** 0·56          **20.** 1·05          **21.** 1·083         **22.** 1·26          **23.** 0·217         **24.** 0·0084
**25.** 0·0066        **26.** 0·324         **27.** 0·5677        **28.** 12·96         **29.** 0·253         **30.** 9·27
**31.** 0·04          **32.** 0·16


*page 34*    *Exercise 3*

multiplication square

| ×   | 0.1  | 0.02  | 0.5  | 8    |
|-----|------|-------|------|------|
| 3   | 0.3  | 0.06  | 1.5  | 24   |
| 0.2 | 0.02 | 0.004 | 0.1  | 1.6  |
| 2.1 | 0.21 | 0.042 | 1.05 | 16.8 |
| 10  | 1    | 0.2   | 5    | 80   |


*page 150*    *Hidden words*

**1.** SOLEIL IS SUN IN FRENCH                  **2.** BEAVERS CUT DOWN TREES
**3.** CAN YOU FIND THE HIDDEN WORDS            **4.** MY CAT CHASES ONLY MICE

*page 152* **Exercise 1**

| | | | | | |
|---|---|---|---|---|---|
| **1.** 5 kg | **2.** 4 kg | **3.** 10 kg | **4.** 7 kg | **5.** 7 kg | **6.** 6 kg |
| **7.** 4 kg | **8.** 4 kg | **9.** 9 kg | **10.** 4 kg | **11.** 3 kg | **12.** 4 kg |

*page 153* **Exercise 2**

| | | | | | | |
|---|---|---|---|---|---|---|
| **1.** 3 | **2.** 17 | **3.** 14 | **4.** 16 | **5.** 7 | **6.** 7 | **7.** 3 |
| **8.** 13 | **9.** 4 | **10.** 0 | **11.** 31 | **12.** 8 | **13.** 5 | **14.** 15 |
| **15.** 7 | **16.** 4 | **17.** 1 | **18.** $\frac{1}{2}$ | **19.** $\frac{2}{3}$ | **20.** 250 | **21.** 0 |
| **22.** 15 | **23.** 6 | **24.** 160 | **25.** 93 | **26.** 26 | **27.** 200 | **28.** 80 |
| **29.** 5 | **30.** 5 | **31.** 1 | **32.** $\frac{1}{11}$ | **33.** 52 | **34.** $\frac{1}{9}$ | **35.** 2500 |
| **36.** 14 | **37.** 411 | **38.** $\frac{2}{7}$ | **39.** 20 | **40.** 400 | **41.** 0 | **42.** $\frac{3}{8}$ |

*page 154* **Exercise 3**

| | | | | | | |
|---|---|---|---|---|---|---|
| **1.** 2 | **2.** 4 | **3.** 2 | **4.** $\frac{1}{2}$ | **5.** 9 | **6.** 2 | **7.** $\frac{5}{6}$ |
| **8.** $\frac{2}{9}$ | **9.** $\frac{1}{3}$ | **10.** 4 | **11.** $\frac{1}{20}$ | **12.** 11 | **13.** 1 | **14.** $\frac{2}{5}$ |
| **15.** 6 | **16.** 5 | **17.** $\frac{1}{6}$ | **18.** $\frac{2}{5}$ | **19.** 3 | **20.** 0 | **21.** $3\frac{3}{5}$ |
| **22.** 4 | **23.** 0 | **24.** $\frac{3}{7}$ | **25.** 1 | **26.** 2 | **27.** 3 | **28.** 7 |
| **29.** $1\frac{1}{5}$ | **30.** $1\frac{1}{3}$ | **31.** $1\frac{1}{2}$ | **32.** $\frac{1}{4}$ | **33.** 0 | **34.** $\frac{1}{4}$ | **35.** $\frac{1}{11}$ |
| **36.** $\frac{2}{3}$ | **37.** $2\frac{2}{3}$ | **38.** $2\frac{1}{2}$ | **39.** 0 | **40.** 4 | **41.** 180 | **42.** $1\frac{1}{2}$ |
| **43.** 16 | **44.** $\frac{1}{100}$ | **45.** 10 | **46.** $\frac{1}{4}$ | **47.** $\frac{2}{3}$ | **48.** $\frac{1}{8}$ | |

Page 156 Ex4
1. $x = 3\frac{2}{3}$  2. $x = 2\frac{2}{5}$  3. $x = 5/6$  4. $x = 1$  5. $x = 10$  6. $x = 2\frac{1}{2}$
7. $x = 1000$  8. $x = \frac{1}{4}$

*page 157* **Exercise 5**

**1.** (a) 51° (b) 41° (c) 100° **2.** $42\frac{1}{2}$° **3.** 63, 64, 65 **4.** 9 cm
**5.** 2·5 cm **6.** 6 cm **7.** (a) 19 (b) 21 **8.** 3·5 cm **9.** 2
**10.** 31 **11.** $x = 12$, parcels 9, 12, 24, 49 **12.** 5 **13.** (a) $4x$ (b) 1·75

*page 159* **Exercise 1**

**1.** A $y = 7$, B $y = 3$, C $y = 1\frac{1}{2}$ **2.** P $x = 5$, Q $x = 3$, R $x = -3$
**3.** A $x = 3$, B $y = 2$, C $y = -2$ **4.** A $y = 2$, B $x = 4$, C $x = -2$
**5.** (a) (3, 2) (b) (1, 5) (c) (7, 3)
**6.** (a) $x = 5$, $y = 2$ (b) $x = 3$, $y = 7$ (c) $x = 8$, $y = 0$ (d) $x = 8$, $y = 8$ (e) $x = 5$, $y = 21$
**7.** (a) $x = 1$ (b) $y = 7$ (c) $x = 2$ (d) $x = 7$ (e) $x = 3$ (f) $y = 3$ (g) $y = 5$ (h) $y = 0$

*page 161* **Exercise 2**

**1.** $y = x + 2$ **2.** $y = x - 1$ **3.** $y = x + 4$ **4.** $x + y = 6$ **5.** $x + y = 4$ **6.** $y = 2x$

*page 163*   **Exercise 1**

**1.** (a) 3232        (b) 345        (c) 0        (d) 58        (e) 8461        (f) 2038
**2.** 3014        **3.** (b) 75%        **4.** 127        **5.** 335        **6.** 25, 2 left over        **7.** £2·15
**8.**

| | 2 | 5 | 6 | 9 |
|---|---|---|---|---|
| 8 | 16 | 40 | 48 | 72 |
| 3 | 6 | 15 | 18 | 27 |
| 7 | 14 | 35 | 42 | 63 |
| 4 | 8 | 20 | 24 | 36 |

**9.** £100 000
**10.** (a) 4 cm² (b) 24 cm

*page 164*   **Exercise 2**

**1.**

| 6 | 9 | 12 | 7 |
|---|---|---|---|
| 15 | 4 | 1 | 14 |
| 3 | 16 | 13 | 2 |
| 10 | 5 | 8 | 11 |

**2.** (a) 71 mm        (b) 7·1 cm        **3.** (a) 75        (b) 450

**4.** 13        **5.** various        **6.** (a) $\frac{2}{4}$    (b) $\frac{2}{97}$        **7.** (a) 8    (b) 4 cm
**8.** (a) 24        (b) 7        (c) 9
**9.** (a) 374        (b) 539        (c) 426        **10.** (a) 46        (b) 2        (c) 3 → 8 → 18 → 38
        265                386                374
        ‾‾‾                ‾‾‾                ‾‾‾
        639                925                800

*page 165*   **Exercise 3**

**1.** 1700        **2.** 60        **3.** 200        **4.** 480 g fruit, 135 g butter, 300 ml milk, 6 eggs
**5.** 17·5%        **6.** (a) 45·6        (b) 12·3        (c) 273·72                **7.** 2 500 000
**8.** 115        **9.** (a) 10 cm²        (b) 13 cm        **10.** (a) 870    (b) 170    (c) 46    (d) 290    (e) 220    (f) 955
**11.** (a) 1·4        (b) 1·7        (c) 0·2        (d) 0·25        (e) 2·1        (f) 0·36                **12.** 10

*page 166*   **Exercise 4**

**1.** (a) 700        (b) 15        **2.** 3·55                **4.** 47, 26p                **4.** 54 × 3 = 162
**5.** 14                                **6.** 6 m/s                **7.**                                        **8.** 440 g

**9.** 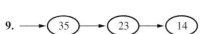        **10.** (a) 1014 mm        (b) 101·4 cm        (c) more
**11.** (a) vertical        (b) perpendicular        (c) horizontal

# Part 5

*page 169*   ***Exercise 1***

**1.** (a) $\frac{1}{4}$ turn clockwise      (b) $\frac{1}{2}$ turn          (c) $\frac{1}{4}$ turn anticlockwise

(d) $\frac{1}{4}$ turn anticlockwise      (e) $\frac{1}{4}$ turn clockwise    (f) $\frac{1}{2}$ turn

**2.**       **3.**       **4.**       **5.**       **6.**

**7.**       **8.**       **9.**       **10.**       **11.** $\frac{1}{4}$ turn clockwise

**12.** $\frac{1}{4}$ turn anticlockwise      **13.** $\frac{1}{2}$ turn      **14.** $\frac{1}{4}$ turn anticlockwise

**15.** $\frac{1}{2}$ turn      **16.** $\frac{1}{4}$ turn anticlockwise      **17.**

B

**18.**  C      **19.**  D      **20.**  E

*page 171*   ***Exercise 2***

**1.** (a) FD 20, RT 90, FD 30, RT 90, FD 10
   (b) FD 30, RT 90, FD 10, LT 90, FD 10, RT 90, FD 20, RT 90, FD 30
**2.** FD 10, PU, FD 30, PD, FD 10, RT 90, FD 20, RT 90, FD 10, PU, FD 30, PD, FD 10, LT 90, FD 20, LT 90, FD 20, RT 90, FD 10
**3.** (a) FD 30, LT 90, FD 20, LT 90, FD 20, LT 90, FD 20, RT 90, FD 10
   (b) FD 20, RT 90, FD 30, LT 90, FD 10, LT 90, FD 10, LT 90, FD 20, RT 90, FD 20, LT 90, FD 10
   (c) FD 20, RT 180, FD 20, LT 90, FD 10, LT 90, FD 20
**4.** (starting at the top of 'L') FD 20, LT 90, FD 10, PU, FD 10, PD, FD 10, LT 90, FD 10, LT 90, FD 10, RT 90, FD 10, RT 90, FD 10
**6.** (a)       (b)

*page 173*   ***Exercise 3***

| | | | |
|---|---|---|---|
| **1.** S | **2.** E | **3.** W | **4.** N |
| **5.** SE | **6.** NE | **7.** NW | **8.** NW |
| **9.** E | **10.** 180° | **11.** 90° anticlockwise | **12.** 45° clockwise |
| **13.** 90° anticlockwise | **14.** S | **15.** W | **16.** SW |
| **17.** N | **18.** 45° anticlockwise | **19.** 135° anticlockwise | **20.** 135° anticlockwise |

**21.** (a) B   (b) H   (c) I   (d) G   (e) F   (f) D   (g) G   (h) A

*page 174*   ***Exercise 4***

| | | | | | | | |
|---|---|---|---|---|---|---|---|
| **1.** Yes, 3 | **2.** No | **3.** Yes, 2 | **4.** No | **5.** No | **6.** Yes, 2 | **7.** Yes, 4 | **8.** Yes, 2 |
| **9.** Yes, 5 | **10.** Yes, 8 | **11.** Yes, 5 | **12.** No | **13.** Yes, 6 | **14.** Yes, 6 | **15.** Yes, 4 | **16.** Yes, 14 |

**1.** 3 **2.** 4 **3.** 9 **4.** 9 **5.** 4 **6.** 6 **7.** 28 **8.** 28 [Question 7 repeated in error]

**1.** 19 possible designs

**1.** Eight different triangles:

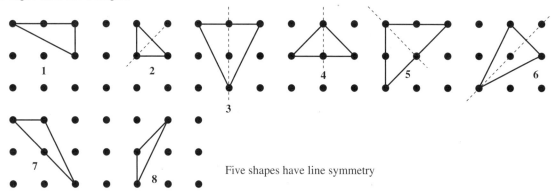

Five shapes have line symmetry

**2.** Sixteen different quadrilaterals:

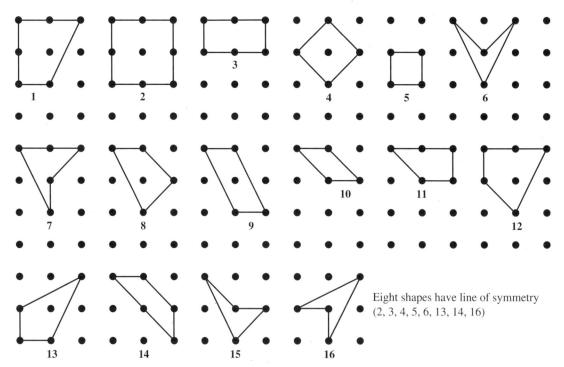

Eight shapes have line of symmetry
(2, 3, 4, 5, 6, 13, 14, 16)

*page 181*   **Exercise 1**

**2.** (a) 2 units right, 3 units down     (b) 5 units right, 3 units up
   (c) 4 units left, 1 unit up     (d) 7 units left
**3.** (e) 2 units right, 4 units down
**4.** 1 right, 2 up; 5 right; 3 down; 2 left; 2 up; 2 left; 1 left, 2 down; 1 left, 1 up


*page 182*   **Exercise 1**

| | | | | | | |
|---|---|---|---|---|---|---|
| **1.** 345 | **2.** 434 | **3.** 512 | **4.** 238 | **5.** 594 | **6.** 456 | **7.** 527 |
| **8.** 676 | **9.** 504 | **10.** 864 | **11.** 728 | **12.** 567 | **13.** 800 | **14.** 891 |
| **15.** 504 | **16.** 945 | **17.** 9594 | **18.** 8662 | **19.** 15 557 | **20.** 9513 | **21.** 3936 |
| **22.** 12 222 | **23.** 49 044 | **24.** 17 982 | **25.** 27·9 | **26.** 1·092 | **27.** 28·98 | **28.** 0·3322 |
| **29.** 377·2 | **30.** 27·01 | **31.** 0·484 | **32.** 4·082 | | | |


*page 183*   **Exercise 2**

| | | | | | |
|---|---|---|---|---|---|
| **1.** 21 r 2 | **2.** 22 r 3 | **3.** 31 r 2 | **4.** 32 | **5.** 32 r 4 | **6.** 42 r 4 |
| **7.** 35 r 4 | **8.** 33 r 5 | **9.** 27 | **10.** 34 r 6 | **11.** 48 | **12.** 32 r 6 |
| **13.** 20 r 11 | **14.** 11 r 12 | **15.** 22 r 11 | **16.** 21 r 12 | **17.** 10 r 7 | **18.** 21 r 22 |
| **19.** 21 r 4 | **20.** 29 r 6 | **21.** 21 r 11 | **22.** 11 r 33 | **23.** 2 r 14 | **24.** 12 r 29 |
| **25.** 22 r 11 | **26.** 51 r 6 | **27.** 31 r 1 | **28.** 14 r 39 | **29.** 10 r 56 | **30.** 21 r 16 |
| **31.** 44 r 7 | **32.** 7 r 8 | | | | |


*page 183*   **Exercise 3**

| | | | | | |
|---|---|---|---|---|---|
| **1.** £9·90 | **2.** 65p | **3.** 759 | **4.** £43·68 | **5.** 37 | **6.** 20, 20p |
| **7.** 13 | **8.** £13·95 | **9.** £27 | **10.** 37 | **11.** 3306 | |
| **12.** 26, 2 | **13.** No | **14.** £24 480 | | | |


*page 186*   **Exercise 1**

**1.** 200 g     **2.** 39p     **3.** 6     **4.** mean first (a) 7·4, 8   (b) 5, 5   (c) 5, 4·5
**5.** 58     **6.** 3     **7.** 12°
**8.** (a) impossible   (b) possible   (c) true   (d) impossible     **9.** 510 kg     **10.** 155 cm
**11.** (a) impossible   (b) possible   (c) possible


*page 187*   **Exercise 2**

**1.** −2°     **2.** 4     **3.** 6     **4.** (a) 6   (b) 6·8
**5.** (a) 6   (b) 6·5   (c) 6·2     **6.** (a) 2 modes: 5 and 10   (b) 2 and 7     **7.** 70 or 1
**8.** 480 kg     **9.** median = 3·5 she wins     **10.** 17     **12.** 5, 11
**13.** AOL mean = 7, range = 3 min   COMPI mean = 6, range = 13 min
   AOL is more consistent although mean time is one minute longer
**14.** 3·6     **15.** (a) 3·64   (b) 3·45


*page 190*   **Exercise 1**

**1.** (a) −7°     (b) −2°     (c) 3°     (d) −12°
**2.** (a) −8°C     (b) 5°C     (c) −1°C, −2°C, −8°C
**3.** (a) 5°C     (b) −7°C     (c) −15°C     (d) 3 am     (e) 20°
**4.** (a) −4°C     (b) −11°C     (c) 7°C     (d) 2°C     (e) −4°C
**5.** (a) down 4°     (b) down 8°     (c) up 6°     (d) up 10°     (e) down 35°

*page 191*   **Exercise 2**

**1.** (a) 11°C          (b) 17°C          (c) 13°C          (d) 8°C          (e) 11°C          (f) 22°C
**2.** (a) $-3 < -2$      (b) $-1 \cdot 5 > -5$      (c) $0 > -3$
**3.** Various answers                    **4.** Test A 5, Test B $-1$
**5.** (a) 9          (b) 5          (c) 11          (d) 5          (e) 16          (f) 7
**6.** (a) $-7°, -5°, -2°, 0°, 7°, 8°$          (b) $-15°, -7°, -6°, 2°, 3°, 21°$          (c) $-10°, -8°, -5°, 0°, 2°, 11°$
**7.** (a) $-4$          (b) $-6$          (c) $-5$          (d) $-3$          (e) 0          (f) $-6$
**8.** (a) bottom of lake      (b) floods, build dams                    **9.** $-23 \, \text{m}$

*page 193*   **Exercise 3**

**1.** $-1$          **2.** $-4$
**3.** (a) $-3$          (b) 2          (c) $-5$          (d) 3          (e) $-3$          (f) $-6$
     (g) $-5$          (h) $-5$          (i) $-7$          (j) 4          (k) 0          (l) $-4$
**4.** (a) $-3$          (b) $-5$          (c) $-6$          (d) $-12$          (e) 4          (f) 7
     (g) $-11$          (h) $-7$          (i) 0          (j) $-6$          (k) $-5$          (l) $-11$
**5.** (a) 0          (b) $-3$          (c) $-5$          (d) 1          (e) 0          (f) $-8$
     (g) $-8$          (h) 1          (i) $-5$          (j) $-40$          (k) $-18$          (l) $-80$
**6.** (a) 2          (b) 4          (c) 5          (d) 5          (e) 4          (f) $-8$
     (g) $-5$          (h) 12          (i) 7

*page 194*   **Exercise 4**

**1.** (a) 2          (b) $-2$          (c) 12          (d) $-1$          (e) $-9$          (f) $-10$
     (g) $-3$          (h) 10          (i) 13          (j) $-10$          (k) 0          (l) $-9$
**2.** (a) $-1$          (b) $-1$          (c) $-8$          (d) $-3$          (e) 0          (f) $-3$
     (g) $-4$          (h) 0          (i) $-7$          (j) $-4$          (k) 5          (l) $-4$
**3.** (a) 2          (b) $-10$          (c) 18          (d) $-6$          (e) $-9$          (f) $-14$
     (g) 3          (h) $-5$          (i) 1          (j) $-21$          (k) 0          (l) $-5$
**4.** (a) $-9$          (b) $-3$          (c) 8          (d) $-2$          (e) $-29$          (f) $-5$
     (g) $-3$          (h) 7          (i) $-112$
**5.** (a) $-2$          (b) $-3$          (c) $-14$          (d) 8          (e) $-5$          (f) $-3$
     (g) 1          (h) $-6$          (i) 1

*page 196*   **Cross numbers without clues**

**1.**

| 3 | 7 | 5 |   | 3 | 7 |
|---|---|---|---|---|---|
| 0 |   | 1 | 2 | 7 | 4 |
| 8 | 2 | 8 |   | 4 |   |
| 5 |   | 1 | 6 | 2 | 5 |
| 1 | 8 |   | 9 |   | 3 |
| 3 | 7 | 1 | 2 | 5 |   |

**2.**

| 3 | 8 | 2 |   | 3 | 1 |
|---|---|---|---|---|---|
| 7 |   | 7 | 9 | 7 | 3 |
| 5 | 8 | 2 |   | 3 |   |
| 0 |   | 5 | 1 | 0 | 4 |
| 4 | 7 |   | 7 |   | 5 |
| 1 | 2 | 7 | 8 | 5 |   |

**3.**

| 8 | 2 | 5 | 3 | 3 | 6 | 4 |
|---|---|---|---|---|---|---|
| 7 |   | 3 | 2 | 7 |   | 4 |
| 6 | 3 |   | 4 | 4 | 8 | 8 |
| 4 | 3 | 6 |   | 5 | 7 | 3 |
| 3 | 7 | 5 | 6 | 1 | 5 |   |
| 6 |   | 1 | 8 | 2 |   | 6 |
| 4 | 2 | 5 | 3 | 4 | 6 | 4 |

**4.**

| | | | | | | | |
|---|---|---|---|---|---|---|---|
| 3 | 4 | 4 | 6 | 2 |   | 2 | 7 |
| 4 |   | 5 | 3 | 0 | 4 |   | 1 |
| 7 | 4 | 5 | 6 | 2 |   | 5 | 4 |
| 3 | 1 | 1 |   | 4 | 8 | 3 |   |
|   | 2 | 8 | 5 |   | 1 | 6 | 1 |
| 5 |   | 5 | 3 | 6 | 0 |   | 1 |
| 3 | 6 |   | 8 | 4 | 7 | 6 | 2 |
| 5 | 3 | 7 | 0 |   | 2 | 9 | 7 |

**5.**

| | | | | | | | | | |
|---|---|---|---|---|---|---|---|---|---|
| 2 | 4 | 6 | 8 | 1 |   | 5 | 3 | 5 | 1 |
| 8 | 3 |   | 2 | 4 | 5 | 8 |   | 5 | 3 |
| 5 | 5 |   | 5 | 6 | 3 |   |   | 5 | 6 |
|   | 1 | 2 | 1 |   | 2 | 4 | 5 | 7 |   |
| 1 |   | 4 |   | 2 | 1 | 7 |   |   | 2 |
| 3 | 3 | 5 |   | 3 |   | 3 | 8 | 6 | 4 |
| 4 | 4 | 6 | 2 |   | 8 |   | 2 | 1 | 6 |
| 9 | 5 | 1 | 2 |   | 2 | 1 |   |   | 8 |
|   | 5 |   |   | 2 | 4 | 6 | 3 | 9 | 1 |
| 9 | 1 | 7 |   | 2 | 1 | 5 | 6 | 1 | 3 |

**6.**

| | | | | | | | |
|---|---|---|---|---|---|---|---|
| 5 | 6 | 3 | 2 | 4 |   | 5 | 6 |
| 6 |   | 2 | 8 | 3 | 1 |   | 0 |
| 4 | 7 | 1 | 8 | 5 |   | 3 | 7 |
| 7 | 6 | 8 |   | 9 | 5 | 2 |   |
|   | 9 | 0 | 2 |   | 6 | 2 | 7 |
| 7 |   | 2 | 8 | 7 | 3 |   | 4 |
| 6 | 9 |   | 5 | 2 | 3 | 1 | 4 |
| 2 | 8 | 4 | 6 |   | 7 | 6 | 1 |

*page 197*  **Exercise 1**

**1.** True **2.** True **3.** False (2 is prime) **4.** True (apart from 0, 1, 2)
**5.** False, 64 is a square number and a cube number
**6.** False, for example $2 + 4 + 6 + 10$ is not divisible by 4
**7.** False **8.** True **9.** True **10.** False (16 has 5 factors)

# Part 6

*page 199*  **Exercise 1**   For discussion

*page 202*  **Exercise 4**

**1.** (a) $\frac{1}{3}$ (b) $\frac{1}{3}$ (c) $\frac{1}{3}$      **2.** (a) $\frac{1}{4}$ (b) $\frac{1}{4}$ (c) $\frac{1}{4}$
**3.** (a) $\frac{1}{2}$ (b) $\frac{1}{2}$ (c) 0      **4.** (a) $\frac{2}{3}$ (b) $\frac{1}{3}$
**5.** (a) $\frac{6}{11}$ (b) $\frac{3}{11}$ (c) $\frac{1}{11}$      **6.** (a) $\frac{1}{6}$ (b) $\frac{1}{6}$ (c) $\frac{2}{3}$
**7.** (a) $\frac{1}{8}$ (b) $\frac{1}{2}$ (c) $\frac{5}{8}$      **8.** (a) $\frac{1}{9}$ (b) $\frac{1}{3}$ (c) $\frac{5}{9}$
**9.** (a) $\frac{4}{11}$ (b) $\frac{7}{11}$      **10.** (a) $\frac{1}{10}$ (b) $\frac{3}{10}$ (c) $\frac{1}{5}$ (d) $\frac{1}{5}$
**11.** (a) $\frac{2}{11}$ (b) $\frac{4}{11}$ (c) $\frac{5}{11}$
**12.** (a) $\frac{7}{12}$ (b) $\frac{1}{6}$ (c) $\frac{5}{12}$ (d) $\frac{7}{12}$ (e) 0, only a Tuna might be able to!

*page 204*   ***Exercise 5***

**1.** (a) $\frac{1}{13}$   (b) $\frac{1}{52}$   (c) $\frac{1}{4}$                  **2.** (a) $\frac{1}{4}$   (b) $\frac{1}{2}$   (c) $\frac{1}{13}$   (d) $\frac{3}{13}$   (e) $\frac{1}{52}$

**3.** (a) $\frac{1}{20}$   (b) $\frac{1}{5}$   (c) $\frac{1}{5}$   (d) $\frac{1}{2}$   (e) $\frac{1}{4}$          **4.** (a) $\frac{3}{11}$   (b) $\frac{5}{11}$   (c) $\frac{1}{11}$

**5.** (a) $\frac{5}{9}$   (b) $\frac{1}{3}$   (c) $\frac{1}{9}$   (d) $\frac{5}{11}$          **6.** $\frac{2}{3}$

**7.** (a) (i) 0   (ii) $\frac{3}{11}$   (b) (i) $\frac{3}{11}$   (ii) $\frac{2}{11}$

**8.** (a) True; she has a $\frac{1}{6}$ chance, Ben has $\frac{1}{7}$
   (b) False; chance for Sarah is $\frac{1}{2}$, but Ben's is $\frac{3}{7}$   (c) False

**9.** 1 red ball and 1 white ball          **10.** 2 white balls and 1 red ball

**11.** 2 red balls and 1 white ball          **12.** 1 red ball and 3 white balls

**13.** B = 20, W = 10, 2 black balls and 1 white ball   **14.** (a) $\frac{1}{9}$   (b) $\frac{2}{3}$

**15.** (a) $\frac{1}{8}$   (b) $\frac{1}{2}$   (c) 1          **16.** (a) $\frac{5}{7}$   (b) 0   (c) $\frac{4}{7}$

**17.** (a) True   (b) False

**18.** (a) ABC, ACB, BAC, BCA, CAB, CBA   (b) $\frac{1}{3}$   (c) $\frac{2}{3}$   (d) $\frac{2}{3}$

**19.** (a) (i) $\frac{1}{12}$   (ii) $\frac{1}{10}$   (b) (i) $\frac{1}{9}$   (ii) $\frac{1}{3}$          **20.** (a) $\frac{4}{39}$   (b) $\frac{4}{39}$   (c) 0

**21.** (a) $\frac{12}{49}$   (b) $\frac{3}{49}$          **22.** $\frac{1}{7}$          **23.** $\dfrac{x}{x+y}$          **24.** Alan did the experiment properly

*page 208*   ***Exercise 1***

**1.** 0·25          **2.** 0·7          **3.** 0·99          **4.** 0·5          **5.** 0·9          **6.** 0·08

**7.** 0·75          **8.** 0·01          **9.** 0·25          **10.** 0·6          **11.** 0·15          **12.** $\frac{55}{100} = 0·55$

**13.** $\frac{8}{10} = 0·8$   **14.** $\frac{8}{100} = 0·08$   **15.** 0·4          **16.** 0·05          **17.** 0·15          **18.** 0·04

**19.** 0·45          **20.** 0·84          **21.** 0·7          **22.** 0·75          **23.** $\frac{3}{5}$, 0·7, $\frac{3}{4}$   **24.** 0·3, $\frac{9}{25}$, $\frac{8}{20}$

**25.** $\frac{1}{20}$, 0·15, $\frac{1}{5}$   **26.** $\frac{12}{16}$, 0·75, $\frac{4}{5}$

*page 209*   ***Exercise 2***

**1.** $\frac{3}{5}$   **2.** $\frac{9}{10}$   **3.** $\frac{1}{20}$   **4.** $\frac{11}{20}$   **5.** $\frac{7}{100}$   **6.** $\frac{11}{100}$   **7.** $\frac{12}{25}$   **8.** $\frac{1}{4}$   **9.** $\frac{1}{25}$   **10.** $\frac{19}{20}$

**11.** $\frac{3}{50}$   **12.** $\frac{11}{25}$   **13.** $\frac{37}{100}$   **14.** $1\frac{1}{10}$   **15.** $2\frac{1}{2}$   **16.** $4\frac{1}{100}$   **17.** $\frac{24}{25}$   **18.** $3\frac{3}{4}$   **19.** $\frac{22}{25}$   **20.** $3\frac{1}{20}$

*page 210*   ***Exercise 3***

**1.** $\frac{3}{5}$          **2.** $\frac{3}{4}$          **3.** $\frac{4}{5}$          **4.** $\frac{11}{25}$          **5.** $\frac{1}{10}$          **6.** $\frac{99}{100}$

**7.** $\frac{1}{50}$          **8.** $\frac{9}{100}$          **9.** 60%          **10.** 44%          **11.** 15%          **12.** $\frac{28}{100} = 28\%$

**13.** $\frac{70}{100} = 70\%$   **14.** $\frac{14}{100} = 14\%$   **15.** 75%          **16.** $12\frac{1}{2}\%$          **17.** $33\frac{1}{3}\%$          **18.** $66\frac{2}{3}\%$

**19.** (a) 25%   (b) 30%   (c) 45%

**20.** (a) 76%   (b) 65%   (c) 80%

**21.** (a) 25%   (b) 20%   (c) 35%

**23.** (a) 27%   (b) 19%   (c) 9%   (d) 60%

**24.** (a) 0·37   (b) 0·42   (c) 0·9   (d) 0·08   (e) 0·06   (f) 0·11   (g) 0·125   (h) 1·2

**25.**

| | | |
|---|---|---|
| $\frac{2}{5}$ | 0·4 | 40% |
| $\frac{7}{20}$ | 0·35 | 35% |
| $\frac{3}{5}$ | 0·6 | 60% |

*page 211* **Exercise 4**

A. MATHS IS NOT HARD     B. DECIMALS MAKE SENSE     C. I CAN'T SOLVE EQUATIONS

*page 213* **Exercise 1**

**1.** (a) 3 times          **2.** (b) 4 times          **3.** (c) 2 times, add 1
**4.** (c) 4 times, add 1     **5.** (b) 'is 4 more than the number of white squares.'
**6.** $s = 3n$; $s = 4n$; $s = 2n + 1$; $s = 4n + 1$

*page 215* **Exercise 2**

**1.** (a) 3     (b) 6     (c) 30     **2.** (a) 7     (b) 35     (c) 700
**3.** 5, 10, 15, 20     **4.** 11, 22, 33, 44     **5.** 3, 4, 5, 6     **6.** 19, 18, 17, 16     **7.** 12, 14, 16, 18
**8.** (a) $2n$     (b) $10n$     (c) $4n$     (d) $11n$     (e) $100n$     (f) $6n$     (g) $n^2$     (h) $2n + 1$
**9.** (a) M5 = 20, M6 = 24, N5 = 22, N6 = 26          (b) M15 = 60, N20 = 82
**10.** 3 : (6, 6); 5 : (10, 10); 40 : (80, 80); 45 : (90, 90)
**11.** (a) (10, 3)     (b) (100, 3)     (c) (101, 1)     (d) (201, 1)
**12.** (a) (16, 4)     (b) (80, 4)     (c) (8000, 4)
**13.** (a) (4, 8)     (b) (10, 20)     (c) (70, 141)
**14.** (a) (120, 2)     (b) (146, 4)     (c) (179, 3)     (d) (201, 5)

*page 218* **Count the crossovers**

For 20 lines, crossovers $= \dfrac{20 \times 19}{2}$.   For 2000 lines, crossovers $= \dfrac{2000 \times 1999}{2}$

*page 219* **Exercise 3**

| | | | | | | | |
|---|---|---|---|---|---|---|---|
| **1.** 44 | **2.** 430 | **3.** 24 | **4.** 51 | **5.** 23 | **6.** 42 | **7.** 18 | **8.** 10 |
| **9.** 7 | **10.** 30 | **11.** 15 | **12.** 106 | **13.** 5 | **14.** 20 | **15.** 66 | **16.** 28 |
| **17.** 90 | **18.** 80 | **19.** 14 | **20.** 24 | **21.** 151 | **22.** 39 | **23.** 5 | **24.** 42 |

*page 222* **Exercise 1**

**1.** (a) 100 km     (b) 1 h     (c) 0815     (d) (i) 60 km/h     (ii) 80 km/h
**2.** (a) 40 km     (b) 0915     (c) (i) 100 km/h     (ii) 40 km/h     (iii) 16 km/h
**3.** (a) $\frac{1}{2}$ h     (b) 1700     (c) 1515     (d) (i) 40 km/h     (ii) 100 km/h
**4.** (a) 1 h 15 min     (b) 1015     (c) 1000 and 1030
**5.** (a) 15 miles     (b) 0930     (c) 50 m.p.h.     (d) 40 m.p.h.
**6.** (a) A, C, B     (b) B     (c) after 36/37 min     (d) 200 km/h
**8.** (a) C     (b) B     (c) A     (d) D     (e) E

*page 224* **Exercise 2**

**1.** 2030          **2.** 1545          **3.** $1637\frac{1}{2}$     **4.** 1500
**5.** (a) 1100          (b) 1045          **6.** About 1325, 37 km from Kate's home
**7.** (a) Robber was caught     (b) 0234
**8.** (a) car C     (b) about 50 minutes

*page 227*   **Exercise 3**

**1.** (a) 20°C          (b) 16°C          (c) 17.00, 22.30     (d) 15.00               (e) 22.00
**2.** (a) 1400 m        (b) 1600 m        (c) 1200 m           (d) 11.00, 13.00
     (e) 2400 m        (f) $\frac{1}{2}$ h        (g) 3 h
**3.** (a) 5p            (b) 5p            (c) 20p              (d) 15p          (e) 5p          (f) 4 min, 6 min
**4.** (a) 30 $\ell$         (b) 15.00         (c) 20 $\ell$            (d) tank filled
**5.** (a) On Wednesday, cold and wet                (b) Monday, Sunday
     (c) On Tuesday and Saturday, it did not rain much but Saturday it was warmer than Tuesday
**6.** (a) Full line for bad weather        (b) About 45 m        (c) 30 m.p.h


*page 230*   **Exercise 1**

**1.** 355                **2.** 84            **3.** £8·30          **4.** 1350          **5.** 4 sacks
**6.** 4, 15              **7.** £5·30         **8.** £86·40         **9.** £489·50        **10.** £210


*page 231*   **Exercise 2**

**1.** £63·00                **2.** £10·23
**3.** 50, 5, 2;  50, 2, 2, 2, 1;  50, 5, 1, 1;  50, 2, 2, 1, 1, 1;  20, 20, 10, 5, 2;  20, 20, 10, 5, 1, 1;
     20, 10, 10, 10, 5, 2;  20, 20, 5, 5, 5, 2
**4.** 0·032, 0·04, 0·334, 0·34, 0·4
**5.** 0·08 mm              **6.** 3784              **7.** (a) 65 536     (b) 4 194 304
**8.** 48                   **9.** $n$, 8·5, $m$        **10.** £22 260


*page 232*   **Exercise 3**

**1.** 46                   **2.** (a) 10     (b) 16     (c) 8     (d) 2
**3.** (a) A = 4, B = 2, C = 6, D = 1        (b) A = 3, B = 7, C = 9, D = 5, E = 1
**4.** 4 (actually $3\frac{3}{4}$ required)
**5.** (a) 0·01            (b) 0·04         (c) 6·54         (d) 14·4         (e) 7872         (f) 254
**6.** 30                      **7.** 5 h 12 min           **8.** 174 years             **9.** 462
**10.** (a) $\dfrac{6+6}{6}$     (b) $7+7-7$     (c) $\dfrac{99}{9}$     (d) $4+4+\dfrac{4}{4}$     (e) $\dfrac{4+4+4}{4}$
**11.** £340


*page 234*   **Exercise 4**

**1.** 240 g              **2.** 14 miles         **3.** 8 km         **4.** (a) $x=2$     (b) $x=1$
**5.** (a) 13·6 g      (b) 50p            **6.** 72%              **7.** 4 665 600
**8.** (a) yes     (b) no     (c) yes      **9.** 57·6 t           **10.** 3960 g           **12.** 64 g


*page 235*   **Exercise 5**

**1.** £625·50            **2.** 225 litres       **3.** (a) 288       (b) $\frac{1}{66}$
**4.** 25                 **5.** £26·10           **6.** 17            **7.** 64 m.p.h.
**8.** 166                **9.** (a) 16, 3     (b) 15, 12     **10.** four
**11.** 50·86 m           **12.** 15

*page 237*  **Exercise 6**

**1.** 38; 12p change          **2.** (a) $852   (b) £281·69          **3.** 0840
**4.** 74 g                    **5.** 1·2 kg is better              **6.** 3·2          **7.** $12\frac{1}{2}$ min
**9.** (a) 105°   (b) 65°      **10.** (a) one: 19/5/95   (b) four: 8/12/96; 12/8/96; 24/4/96; 16/6/96

# Part 7

*page 241*  **Test 1**

| | | | | |
|---|---|---|---|---|
| **1.** C | **2.** A | **3.** C | **4.** D | **5.** C |
| **6.** D | **7.** C | **8.** C | **9.** C | **10.** D |
| **11.** C | **12.** B | **13.** D | **14.** C | **15.** D |
| **16.** B | **17.** D | **18.** B | **19.** D | **20.** B |
| **21.** A | **22.** A | **23.** A | **24.** B | **25.** C |

*page 242*  **Test 2**

| | | | | |
|---|---|---|---|---|
| **1.** B | **2.** C | **3.** A | **4.** D | **5.** A |
| **6.** D | **7.** B | **8.** D | **9.** A | **10.** C |
| **11.** C | **12.** C | **13.** B | **14.** D | **15.** B |
| **16.** C | **17.** B | **18.** D | **19.** C | **20.** B |
| **21.** A | **22.** A | **23.** D | **24.** B | **25.** C |

*page 244*  **Test 3**

| | | | | |
|---|---|---|---|---|
| **1.** B | **2.** C | **3.** C | **4.** A | **5.** B |
| **6.** D | **7.** C | **8.** A | **9.** C | **10.** D |
| **11.** B | **12.** D | **13.** A | **14.** B | **15.** C |
| **16.** D | **17.** C | **18.** A | **19.** A | **20.** C |

*page 246*  **Revision exercise 1**

**1.** (3, 10); $x = 2$, $y = 8$          **2.** (10, −1); $x = 7$, $y = 1$
**3.** (10, −3); $x = 7\frac{1}{2}$, $y = -2\frac{1}{2}$          **4.** (5, −6)
**5.** (4, −8)          **6.** (−4, 7); $x = -6$, $y = 7$
**7.** (−3, 3); $x = 0$, $y = 0$, $y = x$, $y = -x$          **8.** (4, −2)
**9.** (−1, −8), (−7, −2), (−9, −8)          **10.** (−4, 4), (−2, 4), (0, 8)
**11.** (9, 9), (9, 6); $x = 7\frac{1}{2}$, $y = 7\frac{1}{2}$, $x + y = 15$

*page 247*  **Revision exercise 2**

**1.** 120 g          **2.** £35·43          **3.** $67\frac{1}{2}$%          **4.** (a) £5·11   (b) £3·84
**5.** (a) 5, 8, 20          (b) 8, 12, 20          (c) 5, 11, 13, 17
**6.** (a) 13·3          (b) 3·33          (c) 7·16          (d) 1·51
**7.** (a) 51          (b) 46          (c) 18          **8.** 31 cm$^2$
**9.** (a) 6          (b) 7          (c) 1
**10.** (a) 4·9 cm (±0·1)          (b) $33\frac{1}{2}$° (±$1\frac{1}{2}$°)
**11.** (a) $\frac{1}{2}$          (b) $\frac{3}{4}$          (c) $\frac{1}{8}$

*page 248*   **Revision exercise 3**

**1.** (c) (i) (4, −2)   (ii) (4, 4)   (iii) (−2, −2)   (iv) (0, −2)
**2.** (a) 10·2                (b) 6·6                    (c) 27·2
**3.** (a) 25 cm², 20 cm², 45 cm²                (b) (i) 32 cm²   (ii) 45 cm²
**4.** (a) 230 cm            (b) 0·045 kg            (c) 24 inches          (d) 0·26 km          (e) 3000 ml
   (f) 16 ounces          (g) 2·5 cm            (h) 3 feet              (i) 2600 g
**5.** 1 green, 2 yellow, 3 blue
**6.** 9                    **7.** £2·76            **8.** (a) $x = 78°$, $y = 72°$      (b) $a = 40°$      (c) $b = 8°$
**9.** Con. 115·2°, Lab. 126°, Lib Dem 91·8°, Don't know 27°
**10.** 10 min            **11.** (2, 8), (6, 8), (2, 0), (6, 0), (4, 2), (4, 6)            **12.** $x = 2·5$ cm


*page 250*   **Revision exercise 4**

**1.** £39·32                **2.** (a) 5·5        (b) 0·3        (c) 2·4
**3.** (a) $\frac{1}{10}$      (b) $\frac{1}{12}$      (c) $\frac{1}{20}$
**6.** 40, 41, 42, 43, 44                                        **7.** (a) possible      (b) false      (c) possible
**8.** (a) $2a + b + c$        (b) $2a, a, 3a$        (c) $3m + n, 2m + 4n, 5m + 5n$
**9.** $a = 6$, $b = 4$, $c = 5$, $d = 6$, $e = 4$, $f = 5$
**10.** (All cm²)   A = 2, B = 6, C = 1, D = 3, E = 3, F = 3, G = 3, H = 2, I = 4
**11.** (a)

| 3 | 2 | −2 |
|---|---|---|
| −4 | 1 | 6 |
| 4 | 0 | −1 |

(b)

| 0 | 1 | −4 |
|---|---|---|
| −5 | −1 | 3 |
| 2 | −3 | −2 |


*page 252*   **Practice test 5**

**1.** 94 cm²                **2.** +1, ÷4            **3.** (a) various e.g. 690 ÷ 2      (b) e.g. 460 ÷ 4
**5.** $\frac{7}{8}$                    **6.** £44·55            **7.** £1000
**9.** (a) $5 + 3 − 1$        (b) $(5 + 1) ÷ 2$      (c) $(1 + 2) ÷ (5 − 3)$      (d) $(2 + 4 + 5) × 3$ (other possible answers)
**10.** (a) 1 : 4      (b) 20%                        **11.** (a) 96 cm²      (b) 48 cm                **12.** (4, 5)
**13.** £5·40, £8·10        **14.** 184 cm            **15.** 16 km              **16.** $\frac{3}{7}$